Exploring
EARTH AND SPACE SCIENCE

3

COP–EL

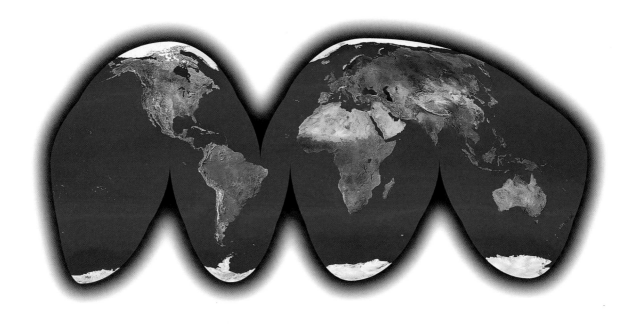

Marshall Cavendish
New York • London • Toronto • Sydney

Marshall Cavendish Corporation
99 White Plains Road
Tarrytown, New York 10591

Website: www.marshallcavendish.com

© 2002 Marshall Cavendish Corporation

Created by **Brown Partworks Limited**

Library of Congress Cataloging-in-Publication Data

Exploring earth and space science.
    p. cm.
    Includes bibliographical references and indexes.
    Contents: 1. Acid and base-Calcium -- 2. Calendar-Continental shelf -- 3. Copper-El
Niño and La Niña -- 4. Energy-Gondwana -- 5. Grassland-Laser -- 6. Light-Meteor -- 7.
Meteorology-Ordovician period -- 8. Ore-Prospecting -- 9. Protein-Star -- 10.
Stratosphere-X ray -- 11. Index.
    ISBN 0-7614-7219-3 (set) -- ISBN 0-7614-7220-7 (v. 1) -- ISBN 0-7614-7221-5 (v. 2)
-- ISBN 0-7614-7222-3 (v. 3) -- ISBN 0-7614-7223-1 (v. 4) -- ISBN 0-7614-7224-X (v.
5) -- ISBN 0-7614-7225-8 (v. 6) -- ISBN 0-7614-7226-6 (v. 7) -- ISBN 0-7614-7227-4
(v. 8) -- ISBN 0-7614-7228-2 (v. 9) -- ISBN 0-7614-7229-0 (v. 10) -- ISBN
0-7614-7230-4 (v. 11)
    1. Earth sciences--Encyclopedias. 2. Space sciences--Encyclopedias. 3.
Astronomy--Encyclopedias

QE5 .E96 2002

550'.3--dc21   00-065801
                                                                                      CIP
                                                                                       AC

ISBN 0-7614-7219-3 (set)

ISBN 0-7614-7222-3 (vol. 3)

Printed in Hong Kong

06 05 04 03 02 01 00   5 4 3 2 1

PHOTOGRAPHIC CREDITS

Casio: *229*
Corbis: *193, 206,* World Panoramas *182–83, 184–84, 212–13*
Image Bank: Alan Becker *196–97,* Enzo Geneletti *202,* Larry Maglott *190,* Mic Melford Inc. *194,*
Terje Rakke *210,* Thomas Schmitt *195,* Harald Sund *165*
Mary Evans Picture Library: *169*
NASA: *174,* Dr. Christopher Burrows, ESA/STScI *166,* Hubble Heritage Team
(AURA/STScI/NASA) *234,* JSC *199,* Planetary Photojournal *237*
NOAA/NGDC: *198*
NSSDC Photo Gallery: *179*
Science Photo Library: *168, 214, 225,* Alex Bartel *222–23,* Dr. Jeremy Burgess *187,* Simon Fraser
216, Steve Horrell *230,* Patrice Loiez *227,* Peter Manzel *204–5,* Lawrence Migdale *228,* Hank
Morgan *226, 232,* Claude Nuridsany & Marie Perennou *220,* Alfred Pasieka *231,* Ludek Pesek *172,
188–89,* Rev. Ronald Royer *208,* Tek Image *175,* Geoff Tompkinson *176,* Dr. Arthur Tucker *218–19,*
Maisonneuve Publiphoto Diffusion *164,* Vincent Realmuto; JPL-Caltech *170–71*

Front cover: The Eagle Nebula (NASA)

Title page: Projection of Earth's land and oceans (Science Photo Library, Worldsat
                International and J. Knighton)

Back cover: The inside of a star (Marshall Cavendish)

Exploring
EARTH AND SPACE SCIENCE

3

COP–EL

Marshall Cavendish
New York • London • Toronto • Sydney

Copper

An easily worked, pinkish-red metal, which is an excellent conductor of heat and electricity

Along with gold and silver, copper was one of the first metals known to humans. Its mineral ores are brightly colored blue-green or shiny yellow, and they attracted attention. At some time someone discovered that, using the heat and charcoal of a simple wood fire, they could produce a red-brown metal called copper from the ores. At least 8,000 years ago, people began making cups, bowls, and jewelry from copper. Archeologists think it is probably by accident that early people discovered that copper and tin ores when smelted (heated) together made a much harder metal called bronze. Bronze is an alloy (A-loy; metal mixture), which could be made into tools and weapons.

Copper became very important. For the people living around the Mediterranean, the best source of copper ore was the island of Cyprus. The Romans called the ore *aes cyprium* (ore of Cyprus). This gave the Latin name *cuprum* to the metal, and its chemical symbol Cu. In English the metal is called copper.

The element copper

Copper is a metallic element. Like all metals, its atoms are arranged in a regular pattern, or lattice, like a crystal. The positively charged nucleus of each atom is surrounded by shells of negatively charged electrons. The electrons in the outermost shell are shared with other atoms. The lattice consists of positively charged parts of atoms, called ions, surrounded by free electrons. This arrangement forms strong bonds between the ions, and it explains why copper has such a high melting point at 1982°F (1083°C). Another feature of copper is that the ions can slide easily past each other. Copper can therefore be hammered into thin sheets or drawn out into wires. In addition, the electrons can move freely through the lattice, making the metal an excellent conductor of heat and electricity.

Copper compounds

When copper forms a compound with another element or group of elements, an atom of copper normally shares either one or two electrons. Each half of the compound is then an ion. When one electron is shared, the copper is in a +1 (cuprous; KYOO-pruhs) state; when two are shared, it is in a +2 (cupric; KYOO-prik) state.

Cuprous compounds include cuprous oxide, Cu_2O. It is used as a red pigment for paints and glass, as a fungicide for seeds, and as an antifouling (protective) agent in paints for ships' hulls. Cupric compounds

A thick cable cut open to show a bundle of copper wires.

HIGHLIGHTS

- Metallic copper has been known to humans for some 8,000 years.

- The United States is one of the world's most abundant sources of copper.

- Copper easily conducts heat and electricity.

- The metal is second to iron in commercial importance and is used to make electrical equipment and piping.

include black cupric oxide (CuO) and blue cupric sulfate ($CuSO_4$). Cupric oxide is used to color glass and pottery glazes green or blue. Cupric sulfate has many industrial uses, for example, as an ingredient in washes for vines and other plants, to kill molds that grow on them. It is also used to make green pigments. Cupric salts, such as cupric sulfate, dissolved in strong solutions of ammonia form a deep blue solution containing the cuprammonium ion $[Cu(NH_3)_4]^{2+}$. This solution dissolves cellulose and was once used to make artificial silk fibers.

Copper resources

Copper in its pure state is found mostly around Lake Superior. About 90 percent of the world's copper ores occurs in four areas: the African central plateau in the Democratic Republic of Congo and Zambia; the Rocky Mountains and Great Basin; central Canada and northern Michigan; and the western slopes of the Andes in Chile and Peru. The greatest single reserve of copper ore is at Chiquicamata, Chile, where the open mine is the world's biggest excavation. More than 160 minerals containing copper are known. Copper was first mined in the United States in 1709 at Simsbury, Connecticut. Large-scale mining began in Michigan in 1845. Today, Arizona, New Mexico, and Montana produce about 90 percent of the copper ore mined in the United States.

Important uses of copper

The properties of copper make it second only to iron in commercial importance. About half the copper used in the United States is for electrical equipment. It can be rolled to 0.0254 mm thickness, or drawn to make thin wire. Copper is also used in piping and plumbing fixtures, although it is increasingly being replaced by aluminum for these purposes.

Copper is also important for its various alloys. Bronze, an alloy of 75 percent copper and 25 percent tin, is still widely used. Brass is 70 percent copper and 30 percent tin.

LOOK CLOSER

The Green Lady

On July 4, 1986, the Statue of Liberty overlooking New York harbor was 150 years old. When she was first given to the United States by France, she was bright and gleaming. The outer copper shell covered a wrought iron pylon, the work of Gustave Eiffel, the designer of the Eiffel Tower in Paris. Over the years, the atmosphere has turned the statue gray-green. The copper began to combine with oxygen in the air, forming a patina (puh-TEE-nuh). Sulfates from pollution and acid rain added to the green color. Because the statue is located by the sea, salt spray also caused the formation of green copper chloride. For her birthday, Liberty was given major structural repairs and was cleaned. She remains a famous symbol of the United States.

The 5-cent coin got its popular name of nickel because it is an alloy of copper and nickel. Alloys of copper and aluminum, called aluminum bronzes, are good substitutes for brass, as they are more resistant to atmospheric corrosion.

Copper is found in small amounts in living organisms. The red blood of vertebrates contains hemoglobin (HEE-muh-GLOH-buhn), an iron-containing compound that carries oxygen. In the blood of many marine animals, such as lobsters, oysters, and cuttlefish, as well as in snails and spiders, the same function is performed by hemocyanin (HEE-muh-SY-uh-nuhn), which contains copper instead of iron.

CHECK THESE OUT!
✔ALLOY ✔ELECTRICITY ✔ELEMENT ✔METAL ✔MINING

Cosmic Ray

High-speed particles entering Earth's atmosphere from deep space

A steady rain of particles is falling onto Earth from space. These particles, confusingly called cosmic rays, come from sources far out in space, beyond the Solar System. Astronomers detect them using the same instruments that other scientists use to detect radioactivity (rays given off by some substances) on Earth. However, they do not fully understand how cosmic rays are produced.

Discovering cosmic rays

Cosmic rays were first discovered in the early 20th century as physicists investigated earthbound radiation. At that time, little was understood about radioactivity. In 1908, German scientist Hans Geiger (1882–1945) invented the Geiger counter. This instrument measured the amount of radioactivity given off by a radioactive source. It showed that no matter how far away the nearest radioactive sources were, there was still a measurable background radioactivity.

Austrian-born U.S. scientist Victor Hess (1883–1964) set out to investigate the source of this background. Hess was an amateur balloonist, and in several flights around 1912 he took Geiger counters to altitudes of around 3 miles (5 km). If the main source of radioactivity had been Earth, there should have been less radiation at higher altitudes. Hess found exactly the opposite. The radiation increased higher in the atmosphere. Hess put forward the idea of cosmic rays bombarding Earth from space. The atmosphere acted as a partial shield, absorbing most of the radiation from far out in space before

it reached Earth's surface. Hess had no idea what these rays might be, however.

Particles, not rays

Cosmic rays were measured from different places to provide more information. More radiation was found near the poles and less near the equator. So cosmic rays must be affected by Earth's magnetic field, which means they must have an electric charge. If so, they must be particles rather than radiation. To measure the charge on cosmic rays, scientists needed a

The violent explosions of supernovas are thought to produce cosmic rays.

HIGHLIGHTS

◆ Cosmic rays were discovered through the radioactivity they cause in the atmosphere.

◆ High-energy cosmic ray particles break up at the top of the atmosphere but cause an air shower of lower-energy particles nearer Earth's surface.

◆ Cosmic rays can be detected with a Geiger counter. A cosmic ray telescope is made by linking two Geiger counters in a row.

◆ Astronomers think cosmic rays are the nuclei of atoms created in the stars and flung off into space in enormous explosions.

LOOK CLOSER

Showers and Muons

Two main types of particles arrive on Earth's surface from cosmic rays. One is the familiar negatively charged electron, which is found in all atoms. The other is a strange particle called a muon (MOO-uhn), which has the same charge as an electron but weighs much more. Muons do not exist naturally on Earth. They can be created only by colliding together other particles at high speeds in machines called particle accelerators. Astronomers discovered that something similar happens in the upper atmosphere. A high-speed, positively charged cosmic ray hits an atom of oxygen or nitrogen, releasing a huge amount of energy. This energy is used to form several other particles with positive or negative electric charges. These particles are unstable and burst apart as they travel through the atmosphere toward Earth (see the diagram, right), forming more new particles. By the time they reach Earth as an air shower, most of the particles have decayed into electrons, but a few survive as muons.

Air showers make cosmic rays easier to find. In space, cosmic rays are so rare that the chances of detecting even one are slim. However, after their journey through the atmosphere, the cosmic rays have produced air showers that spread out, making the original (primary) rays much simpler to detect.

Primary cosmic ray

directional detector. Earth's magnetic field deflects the particles in opposite directions depending on whether they are positively or negatively charged. If scientists could detect the direction from which the cosmic rays were coming, their charge could be found.

The cosmic ray telescope solved this mystery. This device was made by joining two Geiger counters, which detect and count nuclear radiation and particles. Each counter on its own is nondirectional. A particle passing through a Geiger counter in any direction will produce the same output, a click. A cosmic ray telescope links two counters so they record a cosmic ray only if it triggers both counters at the same time. In this way astronomers can tell that cosmic rays must be arriving from one direction.

The first cosmic ray telescopes showed that more particles were arriving on Earth from the west than from the east, which showed that cosmic rays had a positive electric charge. However, as detection methods improved, it became obvious that something strange was happening to cosmic rays in Earth's atmosphere because the particles reaching Earth's surface had negative charges.

Air showers

By studying the particles that reach Earth in air showers, astronomers have worked out what the original cosmic rays are. Most are protons, which are heavy, positively charged particles found in hydrogen and the other elements. A few cosmic rays are larger collections of protons and neutrons (NOO-trahnz), which are uncharged particles present in the nuclei (NOO-klee-eye) of elements other than hydrogen.

All cosmic rays travel at very high speeds. Astronomers believe they are thrown into space by the biggest explosions in the Universe. Some cosmic rays might come from the hearts of huge dying stars that destroy themselves in supernovas, which are extremely violent explosions that briefly appear as very bright new stars. Other cosmic rays could be produced by the even more powerful and mysterious quasars (KWAY-zahrz). Quasars are bright objects rather like stars but they may be much larger and much farther away in deep space.

CHECK THESE OUT!
✔ATMOSPHERE ✔COSMOLOGY
✔MAGNETIC POLE ✔PARTICLE PHYSICS ✔QUASAR

Cosmology

The study of the structure and history of the Universe

Over thousands of years of history, different people have had different ideas about where the Universe came from and the place of humans in it. In the past few centuries, scientific discoveries have changed these ideas completely. The Universe is larger and older than anyone had previously imagined.

The earliest signs that people were studying the Universe date back to the dawn of civilization. As early as 3000 B.C.E., the people of northern Europe understood the movements of the sky enough to build monuments such as Stonehenge, in England, where different stones mark the points on the horizon where the Sun rises at different times of the year.

Early civilizations such as the ancient Egyptians and Babylonians used the movements of the Sun and stars to make calendars and to work out when religious rituals should be carried out. The Egyptians thought the stars were attached to the body of the sky goddess Nut, who stretched from one horizon to the other as the Milky Way. These early cultures thought Earth

Ptolemy thought Earth was at the center of the Universe, orbited by the other planets.

was at the center of the Universe, with the Sun, Moon, stars, and planets moving around it.

The first people to apply scientific methods to understanding the Universe were the ancient Greeks. They tried to find cycles in the Universe to explain how it could work without the constant intervention of the gods. The most successful Greek theory of the Universe was put forward by the astronomer Ptolemy in about 150 C.E. Ptolemy's Universe had Earth at its center, orbited by the Sun, Moon, and planets, with the stars fixed to a spherical shell around the Universe. Ancient ideas of the Universe insisted that orbits had to be perfect circles, so the strange movements of the planets were explained by adding small circular cycles to their orbits.

Ptolemy's ideas influenced many and, most importantly, they were supported by the early Christian church. Therefore, although his ideas were wrong, no one challenged them until the

HIGHLIGHTS

◆ Early civilizations thought the Universe was run by gods who moved other planets around Earth.

◆ In the 16th and 17th centuries, the old Earth-centered theories were swept away and replaced by a Universe with the Sun at its center.

◆ By the 19th century, astronomers realized the Sun was just one small star in the Milky Way galaxy.

◆ In the 1920s, Edwin Hubble proved that the Milky Way is just one of billions of galaxies, all rushing away from the explosion that made the Universe.

16th century. In 1543 Polish priest Nicolaus Copernicus (1473–1543) suggested that the Sun might be the center of the Universe, with Earth orbiting around it.

Copernicus's ideas were not widely accepted until the early 1600s, when Italian astronomer Galileo Galilei (1564–1642) used the first telescope to discover the moons orbiting Jupiter and to prove that everything did not revolve around Earth. German scientist Johannes Kepler (1571–1630) showed that the orbits of planets could be explained if they were moving in ellipses (oval-shaped orbits) around the Sun.

Modern cosmology

In 1644, French philosopher René Descartes (1596–1650) put forward a completely new idea. He said that if the stars no longer had to rotate on a sphere around Earth, then they could be scattered throughout the Universe at any distance. The Universe might even be infinite (IN-fuh-nuht; never-ending).

This change in cosmology led to the idea that the stars might be distant suns. Telescopes had revealed that the Milky Way was made of millions more stars. It soon became obvious that Earth's Sun and the Solar System were not even at the center of this huge system, which

Copernicus was the first to suggest that the Sun, and not Earth, is at the center of the Universe.

LOOK CLOSER

The Big Bang

Cosmologists are still trying to understand the big bang. One of the most important questions they have tried to answer is exactly when it happened. The most recent calculations are based on measurements taken with the Hubble Space Telescope of the most distant galaxies in the Universe. Because these galaxies are so far away, their light has taken billions of years to reach Earth, traveling at 186,000 miles per second (300,000 km/s). By measuring the speed that Earth is moving away from these galaxies, astronomers can measure the rate at which the Universe is expanding. From these results they can then trace back the expansion to find when the Universe started. The latest measurements suggest the big bang happened around 12 billion years ago.

astronomers called the galaxy. Gradually the place of humans in the Universe was becoming less and less important.

The idea of other galaxies existing beyond that of Earth was not accepted until the 1920s, when U.S. astronomer Edwin Hubble (1889–1953) found a new way of measuring the distances to distant nebulas (NEH-byuh-luhz; galaxies other than the Milky Way) by analyzing their light. Hubble changed forever people's views of the Universe. He showed that the nebulas were other star systems so distant that their light takes millions, or even billions, of years to reach Earth.

Hubble also proved that all the galaxies in the Universe are rushing away from each other. Astronomers had always thought the Universe was completely unchanging. Hubble's discovery meant the movements of galaxies could be tracked back to a point where all the galaxies came together. Belgian physicist Georges Lemaître (1894–1966) suggested this starting point was the beginning of the Universe. Astronomers now call it the big bang.

CHECK THESE OUT!
✔EARTH ✔GALAXY ✔HUBBLE SPACE TELESCOPE
✔MILKY WAY ✔SPACE ✔STAR ✔SUN ✔UNIVERSE

Crater

When a volcano explodes or collapses, it leaves behind a nearly circular hollow. This hollow may be at the summit (top) of the volcano or at ground level. Similar pits are caused by the impact of meteorites (MEE-tee-uh-RYTS; small particles falling from outer space). These hollows and pits are called craters.

Volcanic craters

Volcanoes occur where magma (MAG-muh; molten rock) finds a way to burst through a rift in Earth's crust. When it reaches the surface, this magma is called lava (LAH-vuh). Large amounts of gas are also released, often causing an explosion that blows out the volcano's top or sides.

The eruption of lava can leave an empty space below. The surface rocks may collapse to form a circular or oval depression with a flat bottom, called a caldera (kal-DER-uh). Calderas may be a few miles across or as much as 40 miles (64 km) wide. Many volcanic craters occur at the center of calderas. When Mount Mazama in Oregon blew up 7,000 years ago, its remains dropped into the space below, creating Crater Lake. The tops of the Hawaiian volcanoes of Mauna Loa and Kilauea also collapsed, driving out lava through other openings and creating other craters.

Volcanoes can remain inactive for a very long time and then suddenly explode. In 1980, Mount St. Helens, in the Cascade Range of Washington state, erupted after a century of inactivity. The whole north side of the mountain was blown out in a landslide of rock and ice. Its top was replaced by a crater 1 mile (1.6 km) across and over ½ mile (0.8 km) deep.

Impact craters

Many thousands of rocky objects and dust particles called meteoroids (MEE-tee-uh-ROYDZ) travel in orbits (paths) through the Solar System. When a meteoroid's orbit crosses Earth's orbit, the meteoroid plunges into Earth's atmosphere where it heats up and burns. Small meteoroids called meteors (MEE-tee-ORZ) are vaporized or burned up completely. Meteors are often seen

False-color view of the crater of Mount St. Helens, Washington state.

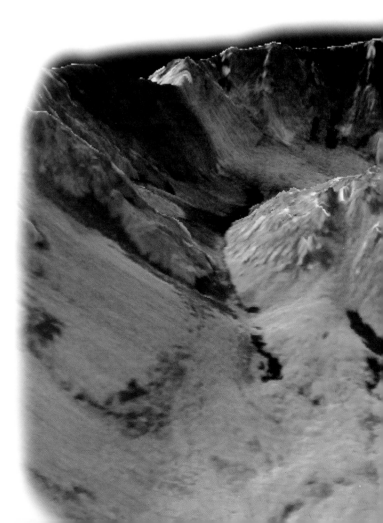

HIGHLIGHTS

♦ A crater is a near-circular depression, left after the explosion and/or collapse of a volcano, or the impact of a meteorite.

♦ Escaping lava through a volcano can leave a space below, causing rocks and lava to collapse, forming a volcanic crater or caldera.

♦ Volcanoes under the ocean are often surrounded by craters and calderas.

from Earth as brief, glowing streaks in the night sky. These are usually called shooting stars.

Occasionally, a larger meteoroid enters Earth's atmosphere, becoming a fireball. Most fireballs explode, but some may not burn up. Those that reach Earth's surface are called meteorites, and are often nearly pure iron. A fireball above Germany in 1916 measured 400 feet (122 m) across but, by the time it reached the ground, it measured only 15 inches (38 cm) across.

There is evidence that huge meteorites have struck Earth in the past. Crater Mound, in north-central Arizona, is an impact crater. Its walls are made of limestone and sandstone. If the crater had been caused by a volcano, the sides of the crater would contain lava. At least 80 impact craters have been found on Earth. The largest single meteorite known is still in its crater in Namibia, Africa. It probably originally weighed more than 110 tons (100 tonnes), but much of it has rusted away to leave behind about 66 tons (60 tonnes) of meteorite in the crater.

LOOK CLOSER — Under the Ocean

During World War II (1939–1945), German submarines operated across the Atlantic Ocean, threatening convoys of war materials to Britain. A program began to map the ocean floor, which led to the discovery of the mid-Atlantic ridge. This ridge is part of an underwater mountain chain that circles the world. A rift (a deep, narrow valley) runs the length of the ridge along its crest. Lava rises through this rift and spreads out gradually to cover the ocean floor. The rift is also the site of a number of underwater volcanoes that have craters and calderas similar to those found on land.

Many other underwater volcanoes have also been discovered. In 1984, for example, scientists found the Axial Volcano perched on top of the spreading edges of the Juan de Fuca Ridge in the Pacific, off the northwest corner of the United States. The volcano was surrounded by a caldera, 300 feet (91 m) deep, which had a solid lava floor.

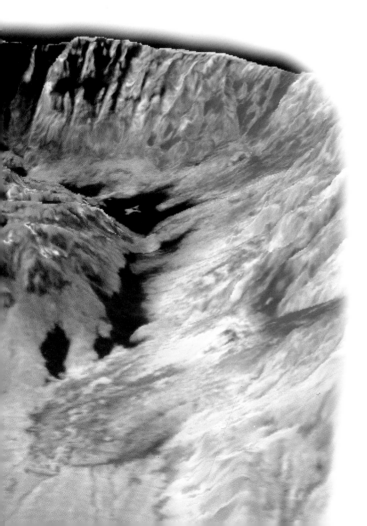

Meteoroids may be debris (duh-BREE) from comets orbiting the Sun. Asteroids are minor planets that also orbit the Sun. Some asteroids have orbits that cross those of other planets. An asteroid or meteorite might strike Earth, causing a great deal of damage and leaving a huge crater. Some scientists believe that a huge meteorite crashed into Earth around 66 million years ago at the end of the Cretaceous period. It was at least partly responsible for the extinction of much of life on Earth, including the dinosaurs. Fortunately, most of the space debris that continues to strike Earth is very small.

Impact craters are common on the Moon, Mercury, and Mars. Most Moon cratering happened over four billion years ago. There is no atmosphere on the Moon to slow and burn up meteoroids and asteroids. Even tiny meteorites leave sizeable craters. Earth's surface was once heavily cratered, but erosion, weathering, and rock formation have removed the hollows.

CHECK THESE OUT!
✔ASTEROID ✔COMET ✔METEOR ✔MOON ✔VOLCANO

Cretaceous Period

**Geologic time period when the dinosaurs ruled
the land and when mammals and flowering plants flourished**

Cretaceous times spanned 142 million years to 65 million years ago and saw the very beginnings of the modern world. The old supercontinent of Pangaea (pan-JEE-uh) finally broke apart. The landscapes and seas were inhabited by the last of the great reptiles that dominated the Mesozoic era. The end of this era was marked by the end of the Cretaceous period and by one of the great changeovers in the history of life. In addition, the remains of billions of microorganisms that inhabited the Cretaceous seas formed today's major oil reservoirs.

The name Cretaceous comes from the Latin word *creta*, meaning chalk. Large parts of western Europe have gently rolling landscapes made of chalk rock. Chalk is a soft and very

white limestone that was originally a seabed mud made of countless limy skeletons of microscopic organisms. The chalk strata (STRAH-tuh; layers) have been molded into low-lying, rounded hills and valleys. Although chalk is too soft for building, it has been quarried since prehistoric times for the flints it contains, to make tools and weapons. Quarrying often uncovered the fossil remains of animals such as the squidlike belemnites (BEH-luhm-NYTS) and ammonites (A-muh-NYTS), and giant sea-dwelling reptiles, which allowed geologists to date the rocks.

Artist's impression of a late Cretaceous landscape. Swamps bordered the seas, and trees and smaller shrubby plants thrived.

HIGHLIGHTS

◆ The Cretaceous period lasted for 77 million years, between about 142 million and 65 million years ago.

◆ Dramatic changes took place in the life, climate, and environments of Earth during the Cretaceous.

◆ By the end of the Cretaceous period, the dinosaurs and their reptilian relatives had died out along with around three-quarters of marine invertebrates.

Layers of chalk and other sediment were also laid down during the Cretaceous in the shallow seas that washed over the Gulf Coast of North America, eastern Russia, western Europe, and western Australia. Lush forests covered the land, the remains of which formed coal deposits in Antarctica, Australia, Canada, and Siberia.

Life in Cretaceous times

In Cretaceous times, the living organisms were similar to those of the previous Jurassic period. However, there were already clear signs of change. Trees were the most common plants in Cretaceous landscapes, particularly a huge variety of conifers, cycads (SY-kuhdz), and ginkgos. However, the flowering plants that are now so common evolved during the Cretaceous as small creeping and shrubby plants.

Animal life on land was dominated by an enormous variety of plant-eating dinosaurs including the huge sauropods (SAWR-uh-PAHDZ) such as *Alamosaurus*, the rhinoceroslike horned ceratopsians (SUHR-uh-TAHP-see-uhnz) such as *Triceratops*, ankylosaurs (AN-kuh-loh-SAWRZ), and duck-billed hadrosaurs (HA-druh-SAWRZ). Dinosaur predators ranged from small raptors such as *Velociraptor* to the enormous carnosaurs (KAR-noh-SAWRZ) such as *Tyrannosaurus*.

Particularly important was the evolution of feathers in one group of small, two-legged dinosaurs. Some of these dinosaurs, known today as birds, were able to fly. The batlike flying

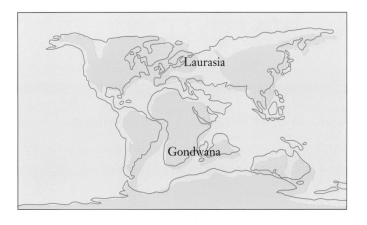

In the Cretaceous period, high sea levels resulted in much of today's land (in blue) being underwater.

reptiles called pterosaurs (TER-uh-SAWRZ) were still common. Other modern kinds of reptiles were snakes, tortoises, and lizards, which had evolved with modern kinds of amphibians such as frogs, toads, and salamanders. Also, small insect-eating mammals became increasingly numerous during the Cretaceous. Some were opossumlike marsupials (mahr-SOO-pee-uhlz), whereas others had more developed offspring when born.

Unfamiliar creatures lived in Cretaceous seas, such as belemnites, ammonites, and the now-extinct reptiles called the ichthyosaurs (IK-thee-uh-SAWRZ) and plesiosaurs (PLEE-see-uh-sawrz).

CHECK THESE OUT!
✔FOSSIL ✔GEOLOGIC TIMESCALE ✔MESOZOIC ERA
✔PANGAEA ✔PLATE TECTONICS

LOOK CLOSER

The End of an Era

The Cretaceous period, and the Mesozoic era, ended with a bang 65 million years ago when a 6-mile (10-km) wide meteorite crashed into Mexico's Yucatán peninsula. The meteorite punched a hole 60 miles (100 km) wide and 7½ miles (12 km) deep. The rock walls instantly collapsed to fill the crater, forming rings of hills and valleys up to 90 miles (150 km) from its center. Firestorms, soot-laden skies, falling temperatures, acid rain, and giant tsunami (soo-NAH-mee) waves caused immense damage to living organisms, especially in the Americas. Whether these generally accepted changes were enough to cause the extinction of the dinosaurs and other creatures, however, is still being argued by scientists.

At about the same time, vast quantities of lava (LAH-vuh; molten rock) and gas poured out over the surface of Earth in western India. This helped change global climates and perhaps started the extinction of some vulnerable groups of animals. The evidence for a meteorite impact, however, was first gathered in the 1970s by U.S. geologist Walter Alvarez and his father Luis, a Nobel prize-winning physicist. In 1981, the impact site was discovered in the Yucatán peninsula in Mexico, buried deep beneath younger rock strata.

Cryogenics

The science of very low temperatures, used in a wide range of applications

When some materials are cooled to extremely low temperatures, often colder than –302°F (–150°C), they can take on a range of unusual properties that are extremely useful for science and technology. The field of science that studies these low-temperature materials is called cryogenics (KRY-uh-JEH-niks).

Creating cryogenic temperatures

At everyday temperatures, the molecules (MAH-lih-kyoolz; atoms bonded together) in any material vibrate and move around rapidly. In gases they move freely, in liquids they are held by weak bonds, and in solid materials they are locked in place by much stronger bonds. In each of these types of matter, however, the individual molecules still vibrate. The material is given its temperature by these vibrations. When an object is heated, the molecules acquire energy and so vibrate more. The vibrations slow down when the heat source is taken away, and the material cools. The coldest possible temperature is absolute zero (–459.67°F or –273.15°C), at which point molecules stop moving completely.

Spacecraft use liquid gases to propel them into space.

In cryogenics, an object is cooled until its molecules hardly vibrate at all. This is done by dipping the object in liquid nitrogen or liquid hydrogen. Nitrogen and hydrogen are both better known as gases, but at temperatures of –320°F (–196°C) and –423°F (–252.8°C), respectively, they condense into liquids, just like steam changing back into water.

Making liquefied gases like these is very difficult. The most common way uses the Joule–Thomson Effect, discovered by British scientists James Joule (1818–1889) and William Thomson (later Lord Kelvin; 1824–1907) in 1852.

These scientists realized that compressing a gas (reducing the amount of space it takes up) increases its temperature, while rapidly decompressing (expanding) it cools the gas. To cool a gas such as nitrogen, it is first compressed and then allowed to cool before being decompressed. This cycle can be repeated several times. Each time the gas loses heat, until

HIGHLIGHTS

♦ Cryogenics means cooling materials to temperatures below –302°F (–150°C), usually by freezing them with a cryogenic liquid.

♦ Common cryogenic liquids include liquid nitrogen and liquid hydrogen.

♦ Cryogenics is used in medicine for cooling ultracold surgical tools.

♦ In the future, cryogenics could be used for freezing organs during surgery or for transplant.

EVERYDAY SCIENCE

A Cool Idea

Cryogenic technology is sometimes used to clean up sites where toxic waste has been dumped. Often, dangerous liquid wastes seep into the ground and form underground pools that have to be removed by drilling down to them. These holes can often collapse, however, especially in loose, sandy soil. Researchers from the University of California found a way around this problem using a drill cooled by liquid nitrogen to –320°F (–196°C). As the drill bit forces its way through the ground, it makes a hole and freezes solid the ground around the hole. When the drill is removed, the hole stays safe until the ground begins to defrost. This leaves enough time for workers to put pipes in place and to remove the toxic waste.

eventually it condenses into a liquid. Cryogenic liquids are stored in a type of thermos flask called a Dewar flask, named for Scottish chemist James Dewar (1842–1923). Unless kept in the right conditions, a cryogenic liquid will rapidly boil back into a gas.

Cryogenic applications

Cryogenics has many uses. Liquid nitrogen at temperatures of around –320°F (–196°C) is used to freeze foods because it freezes them more quickly than normal freezing. Space shuttles are now launched with the aid of liquid gases that have been cooled to very low temperatures.

Cryosurgery uses ultracold tools to cut through tissue. Cryogenically cooled blades reduce bleeding and cut more accurately than normal ones because the blade freezes the surrounding tissue and stops it moving with the knife. Cryosurgery is used to remove tonsils, cataracts, and some types of tumors (TYOO-muhrz; abnormal lumps of tissue).

In the future, cryogenics could be used to freeze organs for transplant and to preserve medical supplies. If

Liquid nitrogen is often used as a coolant for storing biological samples.

living tissue is cooled very suddenly to below –76°F (–60°C), ice crystals will not have time to form. Usually when the water in a living cell is frozen, it forms crystals and expands (gets bigger). This expansion bursts or damages the cell. Cryogenic freezing avoids these problems, allowing the cold storage of tissues and organs.

Physicists are also experimenting with cryogenics. They have found that some materials behave very strangely when cooled close to absolute zero. Some liquids start to become very fast flowing. This effect is called superfluidity (SOO-puhr-floo-IH-duh-tee). The liquids are unaffected by friction (FRIK-shuhn; the force between two bodies) with their containers because the random movement of molecules in the liquid virtually disappears, and all the molecules start behaving in the same way.

A similar effect is experienced by the electrons inside some electrical conductors. This effect is called superconductivity (soo-puhr-KAHN-DUHK-TIH-vuh-tee). The conductor suddenly has no resistance (opposition) to the electric current passing through it. Superconductors are used in machines that must carry a lot of electricity.

CHECK THESE OUT!
✔PARTICLE PHYSICS
✔SUPERCONDUCTOR
✔TEMPERATURE

Crystal

Precious gems such as rubies, emeralds, diamonds, and sapphires are crystals. Many other completely different materials are also made of tiny crystals, including metals, salt, and snowflakes. All these materials are crystalline. The atoms of which they are made are joined in clear patterns. Solids such as glass and plastic are made from atoms joined in ways that do not have a repeating arrangement. These substances are therefore noncrystalline.

Crystal symmetry

Crystals usually have very obvious shapes, such as cubes and hexagonal (six-sided) prisms because of the orderly way in which the atoms are joined in small groups called unit cells. The unit cells are like the bricks in a wall. They join in a repeated pattern to make a crystal. There are many different ways in which the unit cells can join, making different crystal shapes.

These different shapes can be put into a number of groups, which are classified by their symmetry (SIH-muh-tree). Symmetry is a way of telling how regular or balanced the crystal shape is. For example, a cube with six square faces, all at right angles, has a very high symmetry. It looks the same from all sides.

A cube has planes of symmetry. For example, each slice of a cube is square and looks the same as every other slice. The surfaces of these slices are called planes of symmetry. A cube can be turned so that the same view of it appears a number of times. The imaginary line

HIGHLIGHTS

◆ Crystals are solid objects made of atoms or molecules in a repeating pattern.

◆ Crystals are built of unit cells like the bricks that make up a wall.

◆ The atoms in crystals can be joined together strongly or weakly, held by a variety of forces.

around which the cube is turned is called an axis (AK-suhs) of symmetry. The point in the middle of the cube is called the center of symmetry.

Crystal shapes

Crystals will grow well only in certain conditions. Snowflakes, for example, are crystals made when water vapor freezes. They have plenty of space around them so they can grow into well-shaped crystals. Many crystals also form when lava (LAH-vuh) from a volcano cools. These crystals are often small because they are squashed into the rock among millions of other crystals. Some crystals can develop from a salt solution. As the water evaporates, well-shaped salt crystals grow on the sides and base of the container.

Scientists have puzzled over why crystals are held together in

A cluster of clear quartz crystals. Quartz is one of the most common minerals in Earth's crust.

LOOK CLOSER

The Six Crystal Systems

There are six crystal systems, each having crystals with similar shapes. The axis (AK-suhs) of symmetry, an imaginary line around which a crystal can be turned to get a similar view of it, is important in sorting out which crystals go into which system. The cubic system is the simplest; more complicated systems include the hexagonal, trigonal, and orthorhombic systems.

Systems of Symmetry

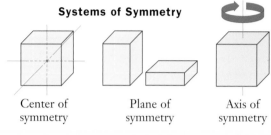

Center of symmetry

Plane of symmetry

Axis of symmetry

Cubic system
(e.g., salt, iron pyrite, and fluorite)

Triclinic (try-KLIH-nik) system
(e.g., feldspar, rhodonite, and axinite)

Tetragonal (teh-TRAH-guh-nuhl) system
(e.g., rutile, zircon, and idocrase)

Hexagonal and trigonal systems
(e.g., quartz, beryl, and apatite)

Monoclinic (mah-nuh-KLIH-nik) system
(e.g., gypsum, orthoclase, feldspar, and tremolite)

Orthorhombic (awr-thuh-RAHM-bik) system
(e.g., barite, topaz, and celestine)

such amazing shapes. The unit cells hold together because some crystal atoms are held by weak bonds and others have strong bonds. The strongest bonds occur when the atoms share some of their negatively charged electrons with other atoms. Diamond is an important example. It is one of the hardest materials known.

Salt, such as table salt, consists of small crystals of sodium and chloride ions. Ions are atoms that have lost or gained electrons and are held together by electrical attraction. Pure metals such as copper and aluminum are usually formed from numerous microscopic crystals. When the metal is bent or stretched, these crystals can slide past each other. The atoms in these crystals do not share their electrons with specific neighbors. Rather, they share them among the entire group, allowing them to move over large distances.

When X rays were discovered by German physicist Wilhelm Röntgen (1845–1923) in 1895, it became possible to look inside crystals. When an X-ray beam is passed through a crystal, a pattern of small dots is created. By studying this pattern, scientists can calculate the arrangement of atoms inside the crystals.

Ordinary light can also be useful in studying crystals. When a light ray enters a crystal at an angle, it is bent toward an imaginary line at right angles to the surface of the crystal. This amount of refraction changes with different crystals, and can help scientists work out the structure of a crystal. Some crystals are useful as polarizing filters, in sunglasses for example. They absorb some light and let the rest through. In addition, if a crystal is in a beam of ultraviolet light it may glow. Crystals with the same shape may glow in different ways, however, which means they have different internal structures.

CHECK THESE OUT!
✔CHEMICAL REACTION ✔COMPOUND ✔GEMSTONE
✔LIQUID CRYSTAL ✔METAL ✔MINERALOGY ✔QUARTZ

Day

Length of time taken by Earth to complete one rotation about its axis

In everyday language, a day is a period of 24 hours, calculated from midnight to midnight, representing one date on the calendar. The word *day* also refers to the hours of daylight, or the time between sunrise and sunset.

As Earth orbits (moves around) the Sun, so it continually turns on its axis, an imaginary line drawn through the North and South Poles. Earth revolves by 15 degrees each hour, so it completes one full rotation (360 degrees) every 24 hours. This time period is called one solar day.

However, the solar day differs slightly from Earth's rotation period as seen from a distant star, which would provide a more accurate picture. This second measurement is called a sidereal (sy-DIR-ee-uhl) day. After turning one complete rotation, Earth must continue rotating for about another four minutes before the Sun returns to its original starting position in the sky. This is because Earth has also moved a little farther along its orbit during the same time.

The world is divided into 24 one-hour time zones, which take into account local national boundaries.

HIGHLIGHTS

◆ Earth revolves at a speed of 15 degrees an hour. It takes 24 hours for it to complete a full rotation.

◆ The solar day is one complete rotation as seen from Earth's surface. The sidereal day is one rotation of Earth as seen from a distant star. It is about four minutes shorter than the solar day.

◆ Atomic time is more accurate than solar time. It is based on the vibration of cesium-133 atoms.

◆ Worldwide standard time is based on Greenwich mean time (GMT).

The sidereal day is 23 hours, 56 minutes, and 4 seconds long, which is slightly shorter than the solar day. Astronomers use the sidereal day for their calculations, but everyone else measures their daily lives in solar time, based on the position of the Sun as observed from Earth.

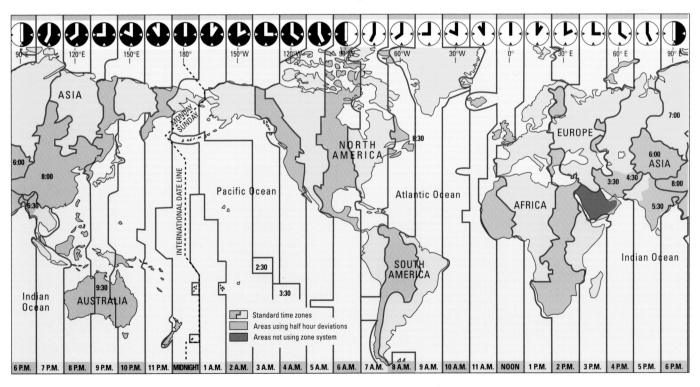

The other planets in Earth's solar system also rotate and experience their own days. The gas giants, Jupiter and Saturn, spin rapidly. One day on Saturn lasts 10 hours 12 minutes. Jupiter's day is even shorter, at only 9 hours 48 minutes. Other planets spin around much more slowly. Venus's solar day lasts 116 Earth days. Mercury completes only one rotation every 59 days.

Keeping time

For thousands of years, humans have used the apparent movement of the Sun across the sky to measure the passing of time. Mechanical clocks keep time at a constant rate, but solar time varies a little during the year because Earth is tilted on its axis and also because it follows an elliptical, or oval-shaped, orbit around the Sun.

The worldwide standard time is called Greenwich mean time (GMT). GMT is based on solar time and represents the local time at Greenwich, England. The main reference point for solar time is local noon, the instant when the Sun is midway along its path across the sky.

Since the 18th century, sailors have calculated their longitude (distance east or west) on ocean voyages by comparing their local time to a chronometer (timepiece) set to GMT. Longitude

At any one time, some areas of Earth experience nighttime while others have daylight.

LOOK CLOSER

Day and Night

In most places on Earth, the length of daylight hours varies with the seasons and with the region's latitude, or distance from the equator (i-KWAY-tuhr; an imaginary circle around Earth, of equal distance from the North and South Poles). Day and night each last 12 hours on the equator all year round. Elsewhere, day and night are equal only at the spring and fall equinoxes (EE-kwuh-nahks-es; around March 21 and September 23). In the Arctic, close to the North Pole, daylight lasts for 24 hours during summer, and night lasts for 24 hours in winter. The South Pole experiences 24-hour days during our winter and 24-hour nights during our summer.

---

is also calculated with reference to Greenwich, since the prime meridian, at 0 degrees longitude, passes through this area in southeast London.

Sensitive instruments show that Earth's rotation, and thus solar time, varies very slightly. Atomic time is more accurate. Atomic clocks measure the rate at which certain atoms, called cesium-133 atoms, vibrate. In 1972, atomic time was adopted as the basis of all scientific timing. Atomic time is now used for the one-second time pulses that are transmitted by radio worldwide. GMT is still used for navigation and astronomy.

Time zones

In the past, each small area of the world tended to have its own local time. This practice led to problems when the railroads came into use, since travelers had to reset their watches many times during a journey. In the 1870s, the world was divided into 24 one-hour time zones. Each zone covers 15 degrees of longitude. Within each zone, all clocks are set to the same time.

Standard time is one hour forward from GMT for each time zone east of Greenwich, and one hour back for each zone to the west. Standard time zones are now recognized by all countries.

CHECK THESE OUT!
✔CALENDAR ✔EQUINOX AND SOLSTICE
✔MIDNIGHT SUN ✔TIME

Delta

The word *delta* was first used nearly 2,500
years ago. The ancient Greek historian
Herodotus (484–424 B.C.E.) compared the shape
of the mouth of the Nile river, where it flows
into the Mediterranean Sea, to the Greek capital
letter Δ (delta). These areas of sediment are not
found at the mouths of all rivers. The Mississippi
delta is the largest delta in the United States.
In India, the River Ganges flows into the Bay of
Bengal through the enormous Ganges delta, on
which millions of people live.

As a river flows, it carries material from its bed
and banks. Other streams flow into the river, also
carrying mud, sand, and grit. In still water or on
the inside of a meander (mee-AHN-duhr; river
bend) where the current flows less powerfully,
the material is deposited as sediment. The
greatest build-up of sediment happens where a
river flows into a body of water such as an ocean.
Deltas have provided rich soil for agriculture
since prehistoric times. Many people live on river
deltas despite the constant danger of flooding.

Delta formation

Typical deltas can be divided into three areas: an
upper delta plain, a lower delta plain, and an
outer underwater platform. The upper plain
begins where the river valley starts to broaden
out. The river splits into many channels, forming
freshwater swamps or shallow lakes. The upper
plain is not flooded by tidal water from the
ocean. The lower delta plain, however, is flooded

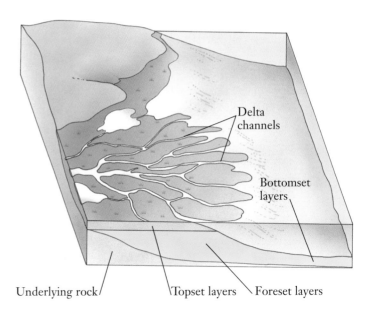

*Deltas are made up of many layers of sediment
called the topset, foreset, and bottomset layers.*

occasionally. The areas between the channels
may include bays of salty water, tidal flats, and,
in the right climate, mangrove swamps.

Delta plains have three main elements.
Channels, levees, and bars at the river mouth
generally contain coarse-grained sediment. Flood
plains, bays, and swamps contain fine-grained silt
and clay. Finally, sandy beaches may be backed
by sand dunes.

The development of a delta depends on the
volume and supply of sediment from the river,
the wave and tidal action, and the water currents.
If the action of the ocean is strong enough, a
delta cannot form. Along the south coast of
New Zealand, the waves and currents remove
sediment as fast as it is deposited by rivers.
Half of the sediment carried into the ocean by
the Amazon River, however, travels 1,000 miles
(1,610 km) along the coast of Brazil to be
deposited near the Orinoco delta in Venezuela.

Forming a delta takes a long time. It begins
when river deposits form a large sandbar at the
river mouth. The bar separates the river's water
flow into two channels. Each channel forms a
sandbar, making four channels. The process

HIGHLIGHTS

◆ Deltas are usually formed at the mouths of rivers,
  where sediment carried from inland is deposited
  as the river loses its speed and carrying power.

◆ Deltas constantly change their shape and size.

◆ The soil that may develop in a delta is usually
  excellent for agriculture.

continues, forming a network of channels, which deposit more sediment farther into the ocean.

The way in which sediment is deposited depends a great deal on the amount the river water is slowed down when it enters the sea. The difference in density (relative heaviness) between the water in the river and the water into which it flows also has an effect. If there is little difference, the inflowing stream slows down quickly and deposits its load of sediment. Ocean water contains salt and is also generally colder than river water, so its density is greater. Fresh water flowing into the ocean will spread across the surface for a long distance, gradually depositing sediment. However, cold, muddy river waters running into a warm lake will quickly sink, flowing out across the lake's bottom, and depositing sediment far from its mouth.

Large deltas can change shape by building outward at rates ranging from a few feet to 200 feet (60 m) a year in a constructive phase. When the delta becomes very large, however, the river has to flow a long way through it and may develop newer, shorter channels in another direction. The delta is gradually eroded by waves in a destructive phase.

Deltas may also sink because the weight of sediment makes the crust sag. The Mississippi delta is currently in a destructive phase. In parts of southeast Louisiana, the land sinks at a rate of more than 1 inch (2.5 cm) a year. New sediment used to be deposited during the spring floods, but dams were built to control the flooding.

CHECK THESE OUT!
✔COAST ✔EROSION ✔FLOOD ✔RIVER ✔WAVES

LOOK CLOSER

Different Delta Shapes

The Mississippi delta is called a bird's foot delta because of its shape. It has toelike sandbars at its channel ends and builds rapidly outward. Deltas that are rounded at their outer edge, such as the Nile delta, are called lobate (LOH-bayt). They move slowly outward over a broad front of sandbars and beaches. Cuspate (KUHS-payt) deltas have a broad point out to sea, where the sediment has been moved by waves and currents. The Mekong delta in Vietnam has this shape. Estuarine (ES-chuh-wuh-ryn) deltas form in the main river channel and do not extend beyond the coastline. The Ganges–Brahmaputra delta in India is an example. The Yallahs delta on the southeast coast of Jamaica is an example of an alluvial (uh-LOO-vee-uhl) fan delta. This type of delta develops when a mountain stream tumbles into a slow-moving river on the plain. In time, the sediment blocks the channel and the stream shifts its course from side to side. The area becomes a fan shape of deposits spreading out from the foot of the mountain.

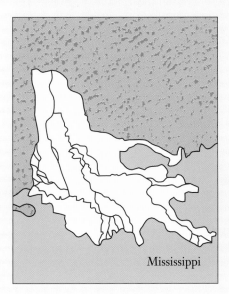

Mississippi

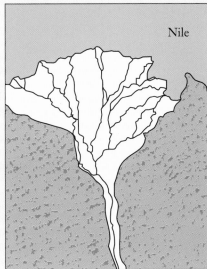

Nile

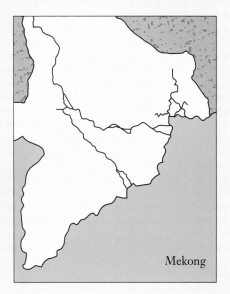

Mekong

Density

In general terms, density is how closely things are packed together. In physical science, the density of a material (its compactness) is the amount of matter, or mass, in a given volume. The amount of mass that packs into a given volume varies from one material to another. A steel ball bearing, for example, weighs more than three times the weight of a glass marble of the same size. The ball bearing therefore is three times denser than the glass marble.

The density of a material depends on the weight of the atoms that make up the material and how closely those atoms are packed together. Gases are much less dense than solids and liquids because gas atoms are much farther apart.

Density measurement

The density of a sample can be calculated by dividing the sample's mass by its volume. Often the mass is easier to measure than the volume. Different techniques are used to find the density, depending on whether the sample is a solid, a powder, a liquid, or a gas.

Because weight is proportional to mass, the mass of a solid object can be measured simply by placing the object on a balance. If the solid is a regular shape, such as a cube, its volume can be calculated from its measured dimensions (length x height x width). If the object has a complex shape, it is easier to measure its volume by dipping the object into a container full to the brim of water and then measuring the volume of

Boats are able to float on water because the air in the hollow hull makes the ship less dense than water.

HIGHLIGHTS

◆ Density is a measure of compactness.

◆ The density of a substance is its mass divided by its volume.

◆ Different techniques are used to measure density, depending on whether the substance is a solid, powder, liquid, or gas.

the water that overflows. The volume of the overflow is the volume of the object.

The density of a powder can be measured in three different ways. First, the solid volume can be measured by pouring the powder into a container full to the brim of liquid and measuring how much water overflows. If the liquid wets the powder but does not dissolve it, the mass of the powder divided by this volume is the true density of the solid in the powder. The average density of the solid and the air between the grains of a powder is measured by pouring a sample of the powder into a measuring cylinder. This is the bulk density of the powder. Soap powder manufacturers need to know the bulk density when designing packets for the product. The third value for the density of a powder is measured by placing a sample of the powder in a measuring cylinder and bumping the base of the cylinder to make the powder settle. This is the packing density of the powder. The packing density is greater than the bulk density but less than the true density of the solid in the powder.

The density of a liquid can be measured by pouring the liquid into a glass bottle, the volume of which is known exactly. The mass of the liquid is then divided by the volume of the bottle. A device called a hydrometer (hy-DRAH-muh-tuhr) can be used to measure the density of a liquid sample. A hydrometer is a type of float that has a weighted bulb at its bottom and a long, thin neck at its top. The density of the liquid is read from markings on the neck: the deeper the hydrometer's neck sinks into the liquid, the lower the density of the liquid.

The density of a gas can be measured by filling a flask with the gas, weighing the flask, and then pumping all the gas out of the flask and weighing it again. The density is the difference in masses divided by the volume of the flask.

CHECK THESE OUT!
✔MASS ✔MATTER

LOOK CLOSER

Relative Density

Densities can be measured in relation to air and water. Hydrogen, which has a density less than one-thirteenth the density of air, was used to keep airships aloft. However, its flammability led to several disastrous fires. Helium, which is not flammable, took the place of hydrogen for use in airships and some balloons. Carbon dioxide has a density one and a half times the density of air. This is why carbon dioxide drifts along the ground when dry ice sublimes (passes from solid to vapor state).

The density of gasoline is two-thirds the density of water, which is why gasoline floats on water. Steel is almost eight times as dense as water. A steel ship floats, however, because the average density of the steel hull and the air inside it is less than the density of water. Silver has a density just over one–half the density of gold.

Desert

The word *desert* usually conjures up a picture of a hot, dry landscape of sand dunes (DOONZ). All deserts are dry and receive less than 10 inches (25 cm) of rain a year, but not all deserts are hot or covered with sand. Both the hottest (Libya) and coldest (Antarctica) places on Earth are deserts.

Deserts are formed by certain climate conditions that produce dry air, especially in the middle of continents, although some deserts are found on the coasts. The dry air prevents the growth of plants that bind soil together. Loose surface particles are blown away by the wind to leave barren, rocky landscapes. Blown sand is trapped in some areas to form sandy deserts.

Deserts cover about 30 percent of Earth's surface. In the past, deserts have been much more widespread, for example, during Permo-Triassic times (286 million to 208 million years ago), Devonian times (408 million to 360 million years ago), and throughout the Precambrian (before 570 million years ago), when there were no land plants to form and bind soils.

Hot deserts

The world's hot deserts are found in subtropical regions. In the northern hemisphere they include the Arabian and Saharan deserts of Africa. The hottest recorded air temperature of 136°F (58°C) was measured in the shade at Al-Alzizyah, Libya, in the Sahara. Around midday the temperature of the Saharan sand can reach 189°F (87°C).

Hot deserts in the southern hemisphere include the Namib and Kalahari of Africa and the Great Sandy Desert of Western Australia. What little rain there is does not fall every year but may be produced by a sudden torrential storm once every few years. Several inches of rain may fall in a very short time and rapidly run off the surface to produce flash floods. The floods dissolve any soluble salts from the rocks and wash away loose sediment (SEH-duh-muhnt; small particles of material) into large, shallow lakes. The flood waters soon evaporate to leave layers of mineral salts and sediment.

HIGHLIGHTS

◆ Deserts form where there are very dry climates.

◆ Deserts can be found in cold high polar regions such as Greenland and Antarctica, and in hot tropical regions such as Australia, North Africa, and tropical America.

◆ About 30 percent of Earth's surface is dry or semidry desert, but only a fifth of these deserts are covered with sand.

Cold deserts

Cold deserts, such as the Gobi Desert in Central Asia and the Patagonian Desert of South America, are found to the north and south of the subtropical hot deserts. They often form on the sheltered (lee) sides of mountain chains. Wind-blown air is cooled as it rises up a mountain. Any moisture that it holds falls as rain because cool air can hold less moisture than warm air. The air that reaches the lee side is very dry. It warms up as it falls down the lee side of the mountain, collecting any remaining moisture present. No rain falls on this side, forming a rain shadow.

Desert landforms

The most famous desert landforms are the sand-seas, the dunes of sandy deserts that make up about a fifth of the world's deserts. The largest sand-seas are in North Africa, Arabia, and Central Asia. The Rub al Khali of Saudi Arabia spreads over 216,000 square miles (559,000 sq km) and has sand up to 140 feet (43 m) deep.

The dunes and sand waves are formed by the wind blowing loose sand in much the same way that sand ripples form under water. Dunes vary enormously in size and shape, from ripples a few inches in height to giant waves 300 feet (100 m) high and 50 miles (80 km) or more long. The shape varies from lines of ridges either parallel to the wind or at right angles to it. Isolated dunes may be star or crescent shaped.

Rock surfaces are polished smooth by sandladen wind, forming an effect called desert varnish. More extensive erosion by the wind carves rocks into a variety of strange shapes. Where the wind removes loose sediment, a pavement of pebbles or rocks remains. The surface of individual pebbles can also be carved by the wind into angular shapes.

Sometimes whole masses of rock are more resistant to wind erosion than the surrounding landscape. As a result, the rocks are left standing like islands above their surroundings. A famous example is the flaming red Mt Uluru (Ayer's Rock) in Australia, which rises more than 1,100 feet (335 m) above the flat desert landscape.

CHECK THESE OUT!
✔CLIMATE ✔EROSION ✔LANDFORM ✔WIND

LOOK CLOSER

Growing Deserts

As the world's population grows, more and more people have to survive on land that can barely support them. Desert margins, the areas at the edges of deserts, are examples of such lands. They are semiarid (SEH-mee-AR-uhd) and get only very little rainfall. Desert margins can support some plants and animals, but they are fragile lands and can easily be damaged by slight changes in climate or by being overworked by human agriculture and grazing animals. The problem has been made much worse by global climate warming, which has caused drought (DRAOOT; extreme, prolonged dryness) and famine (FA-muhn; extreme lack of food), especially in western Africa since the 1970s. As a result, many of the big deserts have grown even bigger, with the Sahara advancing at up to 30 miles (48 km) per year.

The yearly rainfall in cold deserts is also below 10 inches (25 cm), but because temperatures are milder than in hot deserts, more plants can grow and some animal herding is possible in cold deserts. In the polar deserts of Greenland and Antarctica, what little moisture there is falls as snow. The lack of water and low temperatures (down to –112°F, or –80°C) prevent the growth of most organisms except for some algae (AL-jee; plantlike organisms) that can live in ice. There is no sand but plenty of rocky, barren landscapes.

Mt Uluru (Ayer's Rock) in northern Australia is a desert landform that rises over 1,100 feet (335 m) high.

Detergent

Agent that removes dirt and grease

Water alone is not very effective in removing dirt. This is because the dirt nearly always contains grease, which sticks to surfaces and repels the water. What is needed is a detergent.

Soaps and synthetic detergents work in the same way. They are ionic compounds that break up into a positive ion (cation) and a negative ion (anion) when dissolved in water. Usually the positive ion is small and easily surrounded by water molecules. The negative ion is typically much larger, with the negative charge concentrated at one end. At the other end is a chain of carbon and hydrogen atoms, called a hydrocarbon tail. The charged end is easily surrounded by water molecules and so is called water-loving, but the hydrocarbon part is not and so is called water-hating. The water-hating part easily mixes with oil and grease, sticking to it. When enough anions have become stuck to a grease particle, they can surround it with their water-loving ends, so that it can be carried off the article being washed into the wash water.

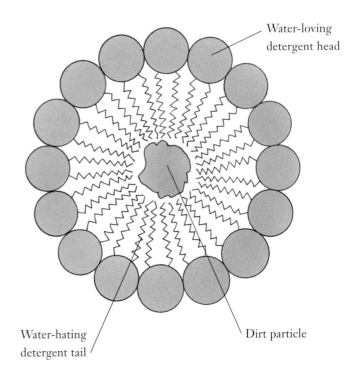

A micelle consists of a fragment of greasy dirt surrounded by detergent molecules.

Detergents also contain chemicals called surfactants (suhr-FAK-tuhnts), which lower the surface tension of water. This causes foaming, which makes it easier for the water to spread across the surface of the clothes or penetrate the materials of whatever is being cleaned.

Soaps

Soaps are the metal salts of long-chain fatty acids. The properties of a soap depend to a degree on the length of the fatty acid chains. Soaps are made by boiling animal fats or vegetable oils with alkalis (AL-kuh-lyz) such as sodium hydroxide (lye) or potassium hydroxide (potash). The soap is separated from the boiled mixture by adding sodium chloride (table salt).

Most soaps are not very effective in hard water. Dissolved calcium and magnesium salts in the hard water react with the soap and form calcium or magnesium salts of the fatty acids. These products form a scum. Synthetic detergents do not form this scum.

HIGHLIGHTS

◆ Detergents are compounds that work with water to remove grease and dirt.

◆ Soaps are detergents made by boiling fats or vegetable oils with alkalis.

◆ Synthetic detergents are more effective because, unlike soaps, they do not form scum with hard water.

◆ Scum is a mixture of insoluble compounds formed by the reaction of calcium or magnesium salts in the water with the soap molecules.

◆ Soaps and other detergents are long-chain molecules. One end of the molecule attaches to the grease and the other end attracts and stays dissolved in water.

Synthetic detergents

The first synthetic detergents were developed in Germany during World War I (1914–1918), when there was a shortage of the animal fats used to make soap. They were not very effective. More successful synthetic detergents were introduced during the 1930s. Although these cleaned well, they could not be broken down by bacteria in water-treatment plants. So the detergents were returned to rivers and lakes with the treated water, where they caused thick foams to develop. These foams covered the surface of the water and destroyed aquatic life.

Biodegradable detergents were introduced in the 1960s. Bacteria in water-treatment plants are able to break down these detergents into smaller molecules, which do not cause foaming when the water is discharged into rivers and lakes.

Recently a new danger to the environment has appeared. A typical packet of a detergent product used to contain up to 30 percent of phosphates, which were added to remove calcium salts from hard water. These phosphates are unaffected by water treatment and end up in rivers, lakes, and the ocean. There they act as food for certain algae (AL-jee; plantlike organisms), resulting in excessive algal growth, which takes up most of the oxygen in the water. This causes other aquatic plants and animals to decay and die.

CHECK THESE OUT!
✔HYDROCARBON ✔ORGANIC CHEMISTRY
✔POLLUTION ✔SALTS

Soapy water coming out of household drains often contains phosphates from washing powder.

LOOK CLOSER

Enzymes in Detergent Products

Modern detergents are very effective in removing dirt and grease, but some stains are difficult to remove, particularly at the lower washing machine temperatures that are commonly used today. Grass and blood stains are particularly stubborn. Some detergent products therefore also contain enzymes. Enzymes are naturally occurring substances that play an essential part in every process of living organisms. They are catalysts, that is, they bring about chemical changes but themselves remain unchanged. Some types of enzymes will cause the digestion (breakdown) of proteins, such as those in grass and blood stains, into smaller, simpler molecules. These enzymes are called proteolytic (proh-tee-uh-LIH-tik) enzymes. Proteolytic enzymes were first added to laundry powder in the 1920s in Germany. However, it was many years later that scientists were able to develop really effective enzymes. These enzymes are produced from a type of bacteria. Another type of enzyme, called lipase (LY-payz), has been introduced more recently. Lipase works as a catalyst enabling the detergent to react with fat molecules, which are particularly difficult to remove.

Devonian Period

Geologic time period lasting from 408 million years ago to 360 million years ago

The Devonian period saw major changes in landmasses and life. Continental plates collided to create great mountain chains where once there had been open stretches of sea. Global climates were warm and sea levels high. The inner regions of continents became hotter and drier, and vast deserts formed. Increasing numbers of living organisms began to live in swampy areas. Fish swarmed up freshwater rivers and into lakes.

In these rivers and lakes, some fish evolved in a way that was to transform the future of life on land—these fish developed limbs. The surrounding oceans flooded onto the shallow edges of the continents. The warm, shallow seas they formed were ideal for coral reefs and for a great variety of marine life, especially new types of fish.

Devonian rocks

The beginning of the Devonian period is marked at a point in rock strata (STRAH-tuh; layers) at Klonk in the Czech Republic. Here, geologists can see layer after layer of seabed sediments (SEH-duh-muhnts; material that settles) and fossils in a slice down through the rocks. At this point, geologists can see fossils that show a definite evolutionary change in the sea creatures over that period of time.

The name Devonian was given to the period by two 19th-century British geologists named Adam Sedgwick (1785–1873) and Roderick Murchison (1792–1871). The name is derived from Devon in southwest England, where they mapped a series of strata containing fossils of sea-living organisms that were different from those of the Silurian period (the period before the Devonian) and the Mississippian period (the

HIGHLIGHTS

- ◆ Earth's first forests grew on lowland landscapes late in the Devonian period.

- ◆ The first four-legged animals with backbones occupied the waters of Devonian continents.

- ◆ The two massive supercontinents of Gondwana and Laurentia moved closer in Devonian times.

period after the Devonian). Farther north and west, from Wales to Scotland, right through to Greenland and northeastern North America, the rock strata record land environments of the Devonian. In late Silurian times, the collision of the continental plates of North America and parts of northwestern Europe formed a single large continent called Laurentia.

An artist's impression of a Devonian landscape, showing the red sandstone and swamps of the time.

A mountain range extended from the Appalachian region through New England, Newfoundland, Ireland, Scotland, eastern Greenland, and northern Scandinavia. Rock debris (duh-BREE; broken pieces) that had been worn away and carried from elsewhere filled great basins on either side of the mountains. Vast rivers connected enormous lakes and flowed across semiarid (dry) landscapes. Gravel, sand, and mud sediments were stained colors of yellow, brown, and red from iron minerals.

Life in the Devonian

The new landscapes of Devonian times were the setting for one of the most important changes in the history of life—living organisms moved into the lowlying wetlands, rivers, and lakes. The growth of tree-sized plants and woodlands was also a feature of Devonian times. Small plants were already growing in the wet muds of lowlying coasts and river banks in Silurian times. These plants were mostly very different from those growing today. There were no flowers or grasses, for example, and the landliving animals were small with jointed legs, such as millipedes.

LOOK CLOSER

Fern Forests

Early Devonian plants grew in bogs and marshes. They were mostly leafless, with a top height of about 3 feet (1 m). Soon bigger club mosses, ferns, and horsetails grew to form the first forests. In mid-Devonian times, the first sturdy, upright-growing club mosses appeared. Their stems were strengthened with woody tissue and so they were among the first tree forms. By late Devonian times, some trees and horsetail ferns grew to around 80 feet (24 m).

For the first time, fish and clams developed in the rivers and lakes. Many of these fish did not have jaws or teeth. Their heads and bodies were covered in tough leathery plates made of a type of bone. More familiar-looking fish with jaws and teeth also developed. One particular group of fish had two pairs of muscular fins. Some were lungfish that could gulp air. From these evolved the first landliving vertebrates (VUHR-tuh-brayts; backboned animals) with four limbs.

The first fossil landliving vertebrates were found in Greenland. Scientists think that these creatures were able to move about on land. The animals' legs seem to have been adapted for swimming, holding on to objects in water, and digging for food in riverbeds. The same adaptations meant their descendants could walk properly on land. These animals became the first amphibious (am-FIH-bee-uhs; able to live on land and in water) vertebrates. All amphibians, reptiles, birds, and mammals evolved from these first amphibians.

The oceans of the Devonian world teemed with new types of fish and sharks. Predators (PREH-duh-tuhrz; animals that eat others), some as large as 30 feet (9 m), appeared for the first time. So too did numerous squidlike animals with coiled shells. Coral reefs grew in warm waters and were populated with a great diversity of marine life: sea lilies, shellfish, and sponges.

CHECK THESE OUT!
✔CONTINENT ✔GEOLOGIC TIMESCALE
✔GONDWANA ✔PALEOZOIC ERA

Diffusion

The even spread of a substance throughout the space available to it

Rotten eggs or a scent placed on one side of a room can soon be detected on the other side because of a process called diffusion. In diffusion, the molecules (MAH-lih-kyoolz; atoms bonded together) move right through the space available to them. Diffusion in gases happens because the molecules in substances are constantly on the move. In a gas, the distance between the molecules is much greater than the size of the molecules themselves. The molecules are free to move very quickly and collide with each other rarely. Collisions between molecules and with solid objects, such as walls, make the molecules in a gas move in all directions. For these reasons, smelly molecules from rotten eggs and scents can travel through all parts of a room in seconds.

Diffusion eventually spreads each type of molecule evenly through a confined space such as

a bottle or a room. When a scent is first sprayed into a room, a small space around the spray contains a greater concentration of scent molecules than the rest of the room. Scent molecules quickly move from that small space until the concentration of scent molecules is even throughout the room.

Smoke is a mixture of tiny solid particles and gas. Smoke particles are much heavier than gas molecules, since each particle may contain many thousands of molecules. For this reason, smoke particles diffuse through air very slowly relative to tiny, fast-moving scent molecules.

Smoke diffuses slowly through air, as its solid particles are much heavier than air molecules. Some of the smoke particles settle as dust.

190

Diffusion in liquids

Diffusion also spreads the color of a single drop of ink throughout a bowl of water. The molecules in a liquid move randomly (without any pattern), just as gas molecules do. However, liquid molecules are much closer together. The collisions between molecules in a liquid are much more frequent than the collisions in a gas, so liquid molecules take much longer to diffuse.

Gases can diffuse through liquids. The diffusion of oxygen and carbon dioxide in blood, for example, is an essential part of animal respiration (energy-producing process). Solids can also diffuse through liquids. However, solids diffuse more slowly than liquids because solid particles are larger and move much more slowly.

Diffusion in solids

Diffusion in solids is therefore by far the slowest diffusion process. Unlike molecules in gases and liquids, the atoms and molecules in solids do not move freely. Instead, they vibrate around fixed positions. At room temperature, there will be a small number of vacant positions. Atoms diffuse by jumping into a vacant position and then waiting for another vacant position to appear nearby. Alternatively, very small impurity atoms can diffuse by squeezing between the atoms.

Some metal powders can be made to stick together by heat in a process called sintering. Atoms in the surfaces of the solid particles exchange places by diffusion and bond the powder particles together where their surfaces touch. Solid gold also diffuses into solid copper, but the process is extremely slow.

Some gases can diffuse into solids. Atoms of hydrogen, for example, can diffuse into alloys (metal mixtures) such as steel. The change in structure caused by the presence of hydrogen atoms in an alloy often leads to it becoming brittle. This can be a problem in chemical plants where hydrogen moves around alloy structures.

Gases diffuse easily into spongelike solids such as zeolites (ZEE-uh-lyts) because such solids contain pores (microscopic tunnels) in their structures. Molecules can travel into these gaps and become trapped.

CHECK THESE OUT!
✔ENERGY ✔GAS ✔LIQUID ✔SOLID

LOOK CLOSER

Dissolving Sugar

When a lump of sugar is added to a cup of coffee, it is normally dissolved into the drink by stirring with a spoon. The whole drink becomes sweet as the sucrose molecules in sugar dissolve and are spread through the drink by mechanical mixing (stirring). If a sugar lump is placed in a cup of cold water, the sugar lump will break up and the water will eventually become sweet, even without stirring to carry sucrose molecules through the liquid. This is because of diffusion. First, water diffuses into the solid sugar lump and starts to dissolve it. Then dissolved sucrose molecules start to diffuse out of the crumbling lump into the liquid around it. After a while, there is an even spread of sucrose throughout the liquid.

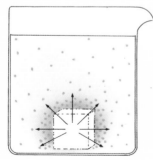

Water moves into the lump; sugar moves out.

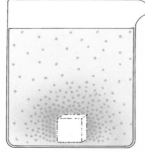

The sugar cube crumbles as the sugar dissolves.

More and more sugar diffuses into the water.

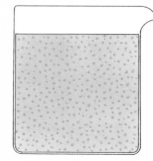

The sugar has moved throughout the water.

Doppler Effect

The change in the frequency of sound or light given by a moving object

Most people are familiar with the way the siren of a police car seems to drop in pitch as it passes by. As the car approaches, the siren sounds high pitched. When the car has gone by, the siren sounds at a much lower pitch, even though the siren is producing a sound of exactly the same pitch all the time. This is called the Doppler effect and is named for its discoverer, Austrian physicist Christian Johann Doppler (1803–1853). Its many practical uses include police radar speed guns, missile guidance, and medical monitoring equipment. The Doppler effect has also been used by astronomers to prove that the Universe is expanding.

How the Doppler effect works

Suppose a person is standing some distance away from a speeding police car. The police car's siren sends out sound waves in all directions. The pitch of the sound depends on the wavelength, the distance between sound-wave peaks. Because the police car is moving, the distance between peaks will be smaller in the direction of motion, giving a higher pitch, and larger in the opposite direction, giving a lower pitch.

HIGHLIGHTS

◆ The Doppler effect was discovered by Austrian physicist Christian Johann Doppler in 1842.

◆ When a moving object reflects light or sound, the frequency of that light or sound is changed according to how fast the object is moving.

◆ Police radar guns, missile-aiming equipment, weather forecasting, and medical monitoring equipment all make use of the Doppler effect.

◆ Astronomers have used the Doppler effect to explain why certain stars appear redder than expected. This has helped them to prove that the Universe is expanding.

Uses of the Doppler effect

Perhaps the best known use of the Doppler effect is in the radar guns used by police officers to check the speed of approaching cars. The same principle is used to measure a range of moving objects. In aircraft, for example, Doppler radar is used to help pilots navigate over long distances. In ships it is used with equipment called sonar to determine the depth of the seabed.

As a train moves forward, the sound waves in front of it are compressed and sound more high pitched. The sound waves behind the train are expanded and sound more low pitched.

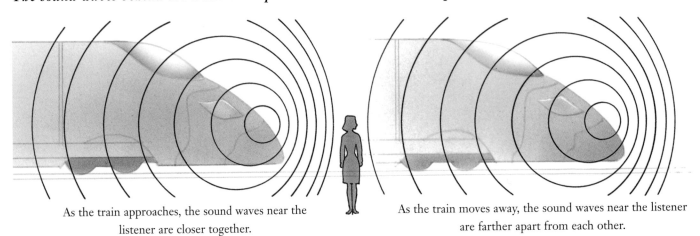

As the train approaches, the sound waves near the listener are closer together.

As the train moves away, the sound waves near the listener are farther apart from each other.

Aircraft can be flown safely thanks to instruments using the Doppler effect to measure the distance of the airplane from other aircraft and the ground.

In the military, Doppler equipment is used to measure the speed of moving targets and so aim missiles more accurately. Weather forecasters also use Doppler radar to work out the speed of approaching tornadoes to give people plenty of warning of their arrival.

Doctors use Doppler instruments to measure blood flow in the human body without the need for expensive and painful surgery. An instrument sends very high-frequency sound waves, called ultrasound, into the patient's body. Because the blood is moving, it changes the frequency of the reflected ultrasound waves, just as a moving police car seems to change the frequency of its siren. By measuring how much the frequency is changed, doctors can tell how fast the blood is moving and whether it is flowing normally. This helps them diagnose the clotting of blood in arteries and problems with a person's heart.

Astronomy and the Doppler effect

The Doppler effect has enabled astronomers to confirm that the Universe is expanding. Stars give off light, but in 1848 French physicist A. H. L. Fizeau (1819–1896) found that this light is sometimes more red or more blue than expected. Light of different colors has different frequencies, and red light has a lower frequency than blue light. If a star appears slightly bluer (blue-shifted), it must be giving off light of a higher frequency than expected. If the star appears redder (red-shifted), the light must be of a lower frequency than expected.

Fizeau realized that the stars must be moving and that the red and blue shifts could be explained using the Doppler effect. Just as a police car siren has a lower frequency as it moves away, so a star's light has a lower frequency (redshift) as it moves away. In other words, the redshift of distant stars and galaxies shows they are moving away from Earth, and this means the Universe must be expanding. The amount of redshift tells astronomers how quickly the stars and galaxies are moving. The most distant ones appear to be moving at half the speed of light.

CHECK THESE OUT!
✔LIGHT ✔SOUND ✔UNIVERSE

EVERYDAY SCIENCE

Police Radar

Police officers sometimes use a handheld radar gun to check that cars are not being driven too fast. The gun sends out a beam of radio waves traveling at the speed of light. When the waves hit a car, some are reflected back toward the radar gun. A moving car changes the frequency of the radio waves slightly due to the Doppler effect. A microprocessor (a computer on a tiny chip) works out the difference between the frequency of the original beam and the reflected beam. It uses this information to calculate the speed of the car and show it on the gun's display.

Drought

A period of abnormally dry weather

A drought is a time of unusually dry conditions. During a drought, crops fail and animals die of thirst. Of all weather hazards, drought is the greatest killer. When a drought brings famine (FA-muhn; extreme shortages of food) to a well-populated area, hundreds of thousands of people may die.

Droughts are usually caused by unusually low levels of rain- or snowfall. They can also be caused by frequent fires or hot, dry winds. During a drought, water is lost from the topsoil through the process of evaporation (ih-VA-puh-RAY-shuhn). Reserves of water deep underground, called groundwater, also run low. Streams and rivers dwindle to a trickle, and lakes and reservoirs shrink. Crops and natural vegetation wither and die. The animals that feed on these plants must move elsewhere or die.

Some types of drought can be predicted, but others happen without warning. Some droughts last only for a short time; others are permanent or last for years. Deserts are areas where drought conditions prevail all year round and are, therefore, predictable. The plants that grow in deserts when there is infrequent rain are able to survive long periods without water. Other parts of the world experience a predictable dry and rainy season each year. Droughts that are not

Irrigation (the artificial application of water to land) has prevented the effects of drought in these fields.

predicted cause the most damage, both to plants and animals. Unpredictable droughts can strike almost anywhere in the world.

Causes of drought

Drought happens when the natural water cycle is disturbed. Normally, water in the form of the gas water vapor enters the air through evaporation as the Sun warms the surface of lakes and seas. Plants also give off water vapor through their leaves. Water is returned to Earth in the form of rain or snow. Some of it wets the soil, the rest runs off into streams and rivers that drain into the oceans. When drought happens, water loss outpaces rainfall. Even a brief period of drought may badly damage the plants and animals of a region. Severe, long-term drought brings widespread famine.

Times of drought often seem to alternate with periods of very wet weather. On a local level, droughts are caused by unusual weather patterns, including changes in prevailing winds and storm systems.

HIGHLIGHTS

♦ Drought is the term used to describe unusually dry conditions caused by inadequate rainfall.

♦ In extremely dry areas such as deserts, droughts can be predicted.

♦ Unpredicted droughts cause the most damage.

♦ Human activities may make droughts worse.

Around the world, areas close to deserts are especially vulnerable to drought. Such areas include West and southern Africa, Brazil, India, and Australia. Once drought has settled on a region, it can spread. The dry air of the drought-stricken region affects local winds and reduces the amount of rain that will fall downwind. The return of rain to a drought-stricken region may also cause problems. During the drought, the region's soil becomes loose because the plants that normally anchor the earth die. As the drought ends, heavy rain may wash away the topsoil and cause mudslides. At first the dry soil will not absorb rain, so the rivers may swell and burst their banks, causing flooding.

Droughts and people

At present, scientists can do little to end a drought. In the modern technique of cloud seeding, rain-bearing clouds can be seeded with dry ice or silver iodide to make them produce rain. However, rain-bearing clouds rarely form in drought-stricken regions.

Many human activities increase the destructive effects of drought. Plowing fields, grazing animals, cutting down trees, and diverting rivers for irrigation reduce the natural moisture in the soil that helps plants to survive in dry weather. These activities also increase soil erosion (the wearing away of the soil).

In deserts, drought conditions are the norm. Desert areas get less than 10 inches (250 mm) of rain each year, which may all fall at once, causing a flood.

STORY OF SCIENCE

The Dust Bowl

Originally, the Great Plains of the Midwest had been covered by grasses whose roots helped to anchor the light soil. By the early 1900s, much of the Great Plains had been plowed up or made into ranchland.

The Great Plains regularly experienced low rainfall and high winds. Then came the drought of 1934 to 1937. Without grass roots to hold the earth together, the topsoil was carried off by high winds. The area became a wilderness of loose dust and bare earth.

The "dust bowl" has since been restored. When the rains returned, farmers planted grasses, drought-resistant crops, and rows of trees to break the wind. They used plowing techniques to reduce soil erosion and allowed fields to lie fallow (unplanted) every other year so that moisture could collect in the soil.

Droughts seem to be becoming more frequent. Some people link this to global warming (the general rise in air temperatures). Others suggest droughts are natural events that have happened through history.

CHECK THESE OUT!
✔CLIMATE ✔EROSION ✔EVAPORATION
✔HYDROLOGY ✔RAIN, SLEET, AND SNOW

Dye

Colored substance that can form a chemical bond with other materials

There are two types of substances people use to brighten clothing and their surroundings: dyes and pigments. Both owe their color to their chemical structure but behave in different ways. Dyes form a chemical bond with the material they are coloring; pigments do not. Colored minerals, for example, are pigments. They are used to add color to products such as paints.

The earliest dyes

The first substances used as dyes came from living things such as plants and animals. A scarlet dye from the roots of the madder plant gave English soldiers of the 18th and 19th centuries their red coats. The food coloring cochineal (KAH-chuh-neel) was extracted from the powdered bodies of female beetles that feed on cactus in tropical America. Some natural dyes are still used today. Henna, which will dye fibers yellow and human hair and skin red, is extracted from the leaves of a shrub that is grown in Asia and north Africa. The only natural dye still widely used is black, which comes from logwood, a tree that grows in the West Indies and Central America.

Only modern dyes could produce the very bright colors in the hair and clothes of these girls.

Just because a substance is strongly colored does not mean that it can be used as a dye. Some natural dyes will color only certain fibers, and they are all expensive to produce. As chemistry developed during the 19th century, people began to think of other ways of making dyes.

Synthetic dyes

The first person to make a dye by a chemical method was a young Englishman, William Perkin (1838–1907). In 1856, when he was only 17 years old, Perkin worked as an assistant to German chemist August Wilhelm von Hofmann (1818–1892) at the Royal College of Chemistry in London. In his little laboratory at home, Perkin tried to make a drug but produced only a black sludge. He was about to throw it away when he discovered that it contained a purplish dye. He extracted the dye and sent it to a Scottish silk dyer. It caused a sensation because all the natural sources of purple were very

HIGHLIGHTS

♦ Natural dyes are obtained from plant and animal sources. Few natural dyes are still used commercially because they are more expensive and less effective than synthetic dyes.

♦ The most important dyes are anthraquinone and azo dyes, which are usually yellow, orange, or red.

♦ Textiles are dyed in a bath of dye dissolved in water. Other chemicals may be used to fix the dyes in the fibers.

Other Dyes

Dyes are often used to color food to make it look more appetizing. Many dyes come from natural sources: green chlorophyll from plants, purple-red coloring from beets, or yellow spices such as saffron and turmeric. Synthetic dyes have also been used, particularly the yellow azo dye tartrazine (E102). Azo dyes can produce allergic reactions in some people. The addition of non-natural colorings to foods is regulated by the Food and Drug Administration (FDA).

Some scientists make use of dyes in the laboratory to stain different kinds of cell tissue. Fluorescent (floo-REH-suhnt) dyes, which glow in ultraviolet light, have been used in the investigation of tumors (TOO-muhrz; abnormal masses of tissue). The red dye Prontosil is an antibacterial agent, and gentian violet is used to treat burnt skin. Finally, there would be no color photography without dyes. Both negative and positive color films and prints are dyed by chemical reaction during development.

expensive. Almost immediately the color became extremely fashionable, particularly in Paris, France. The French named the dye mauve, the French word for the purple mallow flower.

Perkin's success and the wealth it brought him excited other chemists. Perkin had started with the compound aniline (A-nuh-luhn), and within three years a French researcher produced another aniline dye, magenta (muh-JEN-tuh). It was named after the bloody battle of Magenta, which the French had just won against the Austrians. Hofmann himself produced a number of violet dyes.

Another important chemical discovery was made in 1860 by German scientist Johann Peter Griess (1829–1888). He developed a way of producing a range of red, yellow, and brown compounds that are called azo (AY-zoh) dyes. Even today around half of all commercial dyes are azo compounds. After these early successes chemists began to look for ways to make synthetic copies of natural compounds. Madder was synthesized in 1868, both by two German chemists and by William Perkin. Perkin started

from anthracene (AN-thruh-SEEN), a waste product from coal tar that was cheap to obtain, and soon people spoke of coal tar dyes.

The number of synthetic dyes runs into many hundreds. Anthraquinone (AN-thruh-kwih-NOHN) and azo dyes are the most important. The deep orange alizarin (uh-LIH-zuh-ruhn) is an anthraquinone dye. Other dyes have been developed from magenta. Another class of dyes are the phthalocyanines (THA-loh-SY-uh-NEENZ), which are blue and green.

Dyeing textiles

Dyes work only if they fix (attach) firmly to the material. Most are dissolved in water to make a dye bath, and the textile is soaked in it. The dyes make a chemical bond with the fibers. Other ingredients are often added to the bath. One way of fixing the color is to use a mordant (MAWR-duhnt). This makes the dye molecules larger so they become trapped in the fibers of the fabric.

CHECK THESE OUT!
✔CHEMICAL REACTION ✔PAINT

Earth

The only planet in our Solar System able to support life

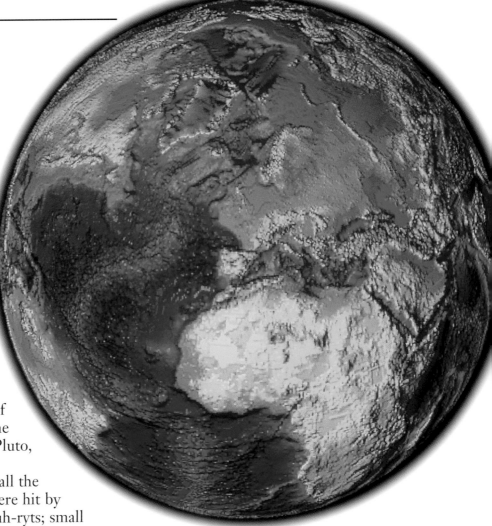

A satellite image of Earth showing Africa, the Arabian peninsula, and Europe.

Around 4.6 billion years ago Earth and the other planets that orbit the Sun were formed. These planets, their moons, many asteroids (AS-tuh-ROYDZ; minor planets), and the Sun make up the Solar System. The closest planet to the Sun is Mercury, followed by Venus, Earth (which is about 94 million miles away from the Sun), and Mars. Each of these planets is made of rock. The more distant planets, excluding Pluto, are made mainly of gas.

Shortly after their formation, all the rocky planets and their moons were hit by countless meteorites (MEE-tee-uh-ryts; small particles of matter). These meteorites made craters, which are easily seen on Earth's Moon. Earth's surface is no longer covered with craters. This is because it is constantly being weathered and changed by the atmosphere.

There have been many different ideas about how Earth was formed. In ancient times, people thought that Earth was at the center of the Universe. In the 16th century, Polish astronomer Copernicus (1473–1543) suggested that Earth revolved around the Sun. This idea was later proved by the observations of Italian astronomer Galileo (1564–1642). These astronomers' early ideas led to a number of different theories about how the Solar System had formed.

Pierre-Simon Laplace (1749–1827), a French astronomer, suggested around 200 years ago that the planets and the Sun were formed from a hot cloud of gas. Modern theories say that the gas

HIGHLIGHTS

- ◆ Earth is the only planet in the Solar System with lots of water and therefore plenty of life.

- ◆ Scientists believe that Earth is about 4.6 billion years old.

- ◆ Earth moves around the Sun in one year and rotates around on its own axis each day.

- ◆ Day and night are caused by Earth making one complete revolution in 24 hours.

- ◆ Earth is not shaped like a perfect sphere. It bulges out at the equator.

- ◆ Earth's crust moves; giant slabs of crust, called plates, gradually move apart and collide, carrying the continents with them.

cloud was cold. Gradually, rocky matter was formed as the gas and dust came together. Gravity drew the material into bigger chunks. Some of these chunks move through space as asteroids. Others grew into large planets.

Life and features on Earth

Earth is a unique planet because it is the only place in the Solar System that is filled with living organisms. Organisms can live on Earth because it is at just the right distance from the Sun for water to exist as a liquid. Water is a precious liquid that is essential for all life. Nearly three-quarters of Earth is covered by the oceans. Mercury and Venus have only hot water vapor and not liquid water. Farther out from Earth, on Mars, water is frozen solid.

Earth is made of three layers. The top layer is called the crust. Below the crust is the mantle, and in the very center is the core. The crust is surrounded by a layer of gases. This layer is called the atmosphere. It contains the oxygen (about 21 percent of the atmosphere) essential to many living organisms. The atmosphere

The Columbia River is the largest river in volume to flow from North America into the Pacific Ocean.

LOOK CLOSER

Earth's Gravity

One of the most important forces on Earth is gravity. This force pulls objects toward each other. Living organisms, including humans, are held on Earth by gravity. Earth itself is kept in its orbit around the Sun by gravity. An object's weight is the strength of its pull by gravity toward Earth. Without gravity, Earth would not have an atmosphere to enable animals to breathe. Because the Moon is much smaller than Earth, it has less gravity. The Moon's gravity is too weak to hold an atmosphere around it. Astronauts on the Moon are not held down so much as on Earth, so they can bounce and jump around on the Moon.

Because Earth rotates on its axis, it has a bulge around its middle, at the equator (ih-KWAY-tuhr; an imaginary circle around Earth at equal distances from the North and South Poles). This is where the Earth has been stretched by its spinning motion. Earth's circumference around the poles is 24,860 miles (40,007 km) and at the equator it is 24,901 miles (40,074 km). The nearer someone is to the center of Earth, the more they are pulled down by gravity and the more they weigh. Someone standing on the North Pole weighs a little bit more than if they stood on the equator. This is because at the North Pole they are slightly nearer the center of Earth than at the equator, where Earth bulges. In addition, since the person at the equator is moving around a large circle at high speed, a centrifugal (sen-TRIH-fyuh-guhl; center-fleeing) force would counteract a small fraction (less than one percent) of his or her weight as measured by standing on a bathroom scale.

absorbs and traps heat from the Sun, making the surface of Earth a pleasant place to live. The atmosphere also acts as a protective shield. Dangerous ultraviolet rays from the Sun are kept out by a layer of ozone (OH-zohn; a form of oxygen with three atoms) high in the sky.

Earth's crust

The continents of Earth have the overall composition and density of granite (GRA-nuht), an igneous (IG-nee-uhs) rock, which means it was once molten. This type of rock has solidified

STORY OF SCIENCE

Flat or Round?

Many years ago, people thought that Earth was flat. They believed there were steep cliffs at the edge of the world and that people could fall off into space. As people began to study Earth more, they began to question this idea. It was noticed, for example, that when a ship sailed into the distance it did not suddenly disappear over the horizon. It would gradually move over the horizon. First the hull disappeared, followed by the tops of the masts. This made people think that perhaps Earth was a sphere and not flat. There was other evidence, too. Sailors noticed that as they traveled north they saw different stars and constellations in the night sky. The stars they saw at home were no longer there. If they were sailing on a sphere-shaped Earth, these observations could be explained.

In addition, when an eclipse of the Moon takes place, Earth's shadow falls on the Moon. This shadow is round, the type of shadow that only a sphere could produce. So for hundreds of years people have believed Earth to be round. They have been able to prove it by using simple observations such as these. Today, people have the most striking evidence possible—photographs taken from space. These show Earth as a beautiful sphere with large landmasses and oceans, swirling cloud patterns, and ice caps.

deep in Earth's crust from molten rock called magma (MAG-muh). Many other rocks also appear in the continental crust. These rocks include sedimentary (seh-duh-MEN-tuh-ree) rocks made of sand, clay, and pebbles. There are also metamorphic (MEH-tuh-MAWR-fik) rocks, which have been changed by heat or the pressures caused when continents move about. Marble is metamorphosed (MEH-tuh-MAWR-fohzd; changed) limestone. The continental crust may be 60 miles (96 km) thick.

Mountain chains are a typical feature of the continents. These chains run in narrow bands, usually where two old landmasses have collided. One of the longest mountain chains runs from the Pyrenees (PIR-uh-neez) in Spain through the Alps to the Himalayas. The highest point on Earth is Mount Everest in the Himalayas, which peaks at a height of around 5½ miles (9 km).

Land is constantly attacked by extreme forces. Water is the most powerful of these. Rapidly running rivers cut deep valleys, frozen glaciers carve away the mountain summit, and seas batter the coastline. The fragments worn away from the land, such as pebbles and sand, are deposited in the sea. There they form new sedimentary rock layers such as sandstone.

Oceans

The floors of the oceans are made of basalt (buh-SAWLT), which is a volcanic rock that has cooled from molten lava (LAH-vuh). The sea

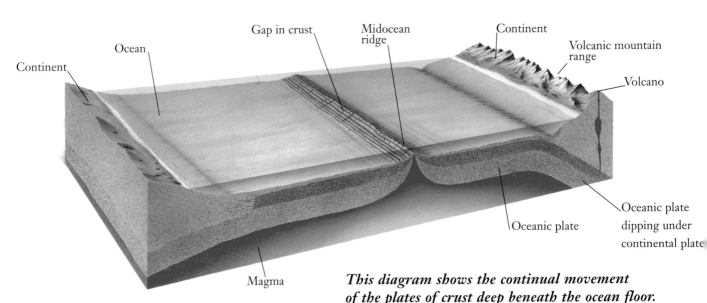

This diagram shows the continual movement of the plates of crust deep beneath the ocean floor.

Structure of Earth

This is a cross section through Earth. It shows in different colors the crust, mantle, and core. Earth's crust is a mixture of thin ocean crust and thicker continental crust. Below this is the mantle, which reaches down about 1,800 miles (2,900 km). The core is in the very center.

The mantle is separated from the crust by the Moho discontinuity, a zone through which the rocks change. It is named for the Croatian scientist, Andrija Mohorovičić (1857–1936), who discovered it by studying earthquake shock waves. The Gutenberg discontinuity separates the mantle from the core. This was discovered in a similar way by U.S. scientist Beno Gutenberg (1889–1960).

The hydrosphere is the area covered by the oceans. The lithosphere is the part of Earth made of solid rock, including the crust and the very top of the mantle. Below the lithosphere, the mantle rock becomes more plastic.

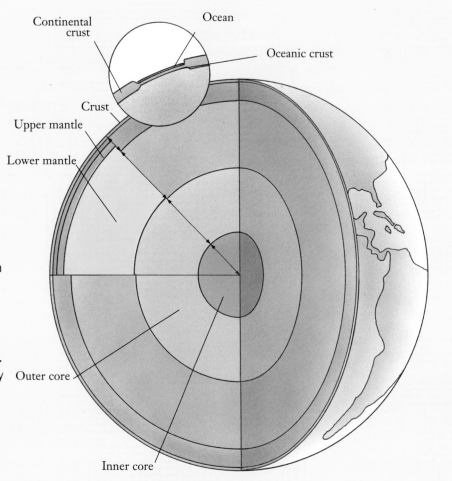

This section through Earth shows the three-layer structure of crust, mantle, and core.

bed is often only 8 miles (13 km) thick and is very young. It is unusual for it to be as much as 100 million years old.

The continents and oceans have not always been the same. A visitor to Earth 100 million years ago could have walked from Africa to America because the continents were joined together to form one huge continent called Pangaea (pan-JEE-uh). The Atlantic Ocean that separates the continents today did not exist then.

The large continents have moved ever since they were formed. When they split apart, an ocean forms. The ocean floor is made by basalt lava that rises to fill the split as the ocean gets wider. High volcanic mountain chains are formed by this lava erupting on the sea bed. These chains are called the midocean ridge. One of these chains stretches from Iceland in the north to the southern Atlantic. If two continents move together, the ocean between them is destroyed. Because the ocean floor basalt is heavier than the continental rock, the basalt sinks below the granite. Here a deep ocean trench will be formed as the sea bed is dragged down. In the central Pacific Ocean, red hot lava has created the Hawaiian Islands. Here the mountains rising from the sea bed are much higher than Mount Everest is above sea level on land.

Continental drift

The movement of the continents is called continental drift. The coastlines of west Africa and the eastern side of South America, for example, look as though they would fit together like pieces in a jigsaw puzzle. Geologists have proved these continents used to be joined by studying the rocks in each area.

When Africa and South America began to drift apart about 100 million years ago, similar events took place all around Earth. Scientists think that the continents ride on huge rocky plates. Plate tectonics is the name given to the theory about how and why these plates move. This theory is used to explain the present positions of both continents and oceans.

The fluid lava released by erupting volcanoes can cover a very wide area.

The mantle

Below Earth's crust there is a thick layer called the mantle. If someone were to travel to the center of Earth, the mantle would start at only about 8 miles (13 km) below the seabed. If the journey began in the middle of a large continent, however, the top of the mantle would be discovered much farther down. It would not be reached until about 60 miles (96 km) below that surface of Earth.

Mantle rock is much denser than most of the rocks in Earth's crust. The boundary between the bottom of the crust and the mantle is called the Moho (MOH-hoh) discontinuity. This is a short version of the name of the man who discovered it, Croatian scientist Andrija Mohorovičić (1857–1936). He found where the change in rock density occurs by studying the shock waves from earthquakes. He realized that some of these waves were slowed down at a certain depth. This is the base of the crust, where the rocks change. The temperatures in the mantle are very high at well over 1832°F (1000°C). This is easily hot enough to melt rock on Earth's surface. Because the pressure in the mantle is very high, however, melting does not often occur. If mantle rock moves upward quickly without cooling, it can become molten. Lava coming out of volcanoes is made in this way.

The great heat in the mantle may cause convection currents to form deep inside Earth. Heat rises toward the crust, and as the rock cools the current falls back into the deep mantle. This is just like the current formed when a pan of water is heated. The hot water rises in the middle and then falls down the sides of the pan as it cools. Two convection cells are formed, one on each side of the pan. Scientists think these currents of heat in the mantle move the continental crust. As the journey through the mantle continues, the rocks become hotter and the pressure increases. At a depth of 1,550 miles (2,500 km), another definite change occurs as the deepest layer, the core, is approached.

The core

The core is the densest and deepest part of Earth. The rocky metal of which it is made is not like anything formed on the surface. The core

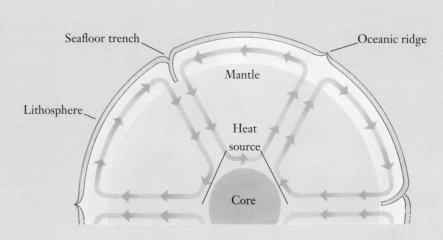

LOOK CLOSER

How Earth May Move

Earth's core is very hot and convection currents rise from it, which form patterns. As the currents cool and reach the top of the mantle, they drag the base of the lithosphere (solid rock) and make Earth's crust move. Where two currents rise, volcanoes form. Where two currents meet near the surface, the seabed is dragged down to make a deep sea trench.

Seafloor trench

Oceanic ridge

Mantle

Lithosphere

Heat source

Core

Convection currents flowing through Earth's mantle.

begins at a depth of about 1,800 miles (2,900 km). A change in rock density occurs here, which is called the Gutenberg discontinuity. It is named for the U.S. scientist who discovered it. Beno Gutenberg (1889–1960) studied the shock waves from earthquakes and noted the way they changed at this depth.

Scientists think that the core is composed of two parts. The outer core is made of liquid metal and the inner core solid metal. The inner core starts 3,200 miles (5,150 km) from the surface. The metals are probably iron and nickel. There is evidence from outer space for the composition of the core. Meteorites fall to Earth all the time. Many of them are made of iron and nickel. Other meteorites are rocky. Scientists think that meteorites formed at the same time as Earth. They are probably the densest lumps of space debris. Scientists believe that the core of Earth has a similar composition to these meteorites. Earth's metallic core also gives the planet its magnetic field, which some scientists believe has an important influence on many living organisms.

The movement of Earth

Although humans may feel safe and still on Earth, the planet is flying at great speed through the space. Earth moves around the Sun at about 65,800 miles per hour (106,000 km/h) on its orbit. A complete journey around the Sun takes a whole year. Earth's orbit around the Sun is not a perfect circle but is slightly oval. Earth is closest to the Sun in January and farthest away in July.

Earth also turns around on its axis. This movement is like that of a spinning top. The axis is an imaginary line running through Earth from the North Pole to the South Pole. It is not vertical, but tilted over at 23 degrees and 30 minutes. Because of this tilt, different parts of Earth are tilted toward the Sun at different times of the year. In June the Northern Hemisphere is tilted toward the Sun and gets its summer. In December it is winter in the north because the Northern Hemisphere is tilted away from the Sun.

If Earth could be seen from above the North Pole, it would be turning in a counterclockwise direction. It takes one day to make a complete turn. Because of this turning, Earth experiences night and day. When the part of Earth on which someone lives is turned away from the Sun, it is nighttime. As Earth continues to turn, so the Sun rises and day begins. Because Earth turns counterclockwise, the Sun rises in the east and sets in the west.

CHECK THESE OUT!
✔ATMOSPHERE ✔BIOSPHERE ✔CONTINENT
✔DAY ✔EQUINOX AND SOLSTICE ✔GRAVITY
✔MIDNIGHT SUN ✔MOON ✔PLATE TECTONICS
✔SEASON ✔SOLAR SYSTEM ✔SUN

Earthquake

Destructive shock wave caused by movement of rock within Earth's crust

One of the most terrifying and unpredictable of all natural forces is an earthquake. Nowhere on Earth is completely free from the threat of earthquakes. In some areas, such as California, earthquakes are common. When an earthquake strikes a well-populated region, many people may die and millions of dollars of damage may be caused.

What causes earthquakes?

Earthquakes do not happen randomly. They are caused by the movement of rock within Earth's crust. The outer shell of Earth is not one continuous layer. It is made of about a dozen huge tectonic (tek-TAH-nik) plates. These plates fit together like pieces of a giant jigsaw puzzle. Convection currents deep within Earth cause the plates to move very slowly. They may collide, drift apart, or grind against one another. Most significant earthquakes occur on the boundaries between plates, on the crack or fault line.

Two rock slabs moving against each other can stretch to absorb a certain amount of increasing pressure. When the movement and the pressure continue, however, the rocks suddenly slip past each other, or one mass of rock slips beneath or over another. This sudden rock movement is the earthquake. Tension is released as the rocks along the fault snap into a new position. The cracking caused by the earthquake sends shock waves called seismic (SYZ-mik) waves surging through Earth.

Earthquakes begin deep underground, mostly in a zone 10 to 20 miles (16 to 32 km) below Earth's surface. The point at which the rocks first break is called the earthquake's focus. The damage caused by the earthquake is often greatest at the epicenter (the place on Earth's surface directly above the focus).

Effects of earthquakes

The first shock waves released by an earthquake are called primary or P-waves. They race through the crust at speeds of 3 to 4 miles (5 to 6.5 km) a second. P-waves are followed by secondary or S waves. These travel more slowly, at about 2 miles (3 km) a second. When they reach the surface, some shock waves become surface waves. These seismic waves cause severe vibrations (tremors), that shake the surface, bringing buildings crashing to the ground.

As well as producing powerful shock waves, earthquakes have other destructive effects. They sometimes make the ground liquefy (turn to liquid). When very wet soil or sand is shaken violently, for example, the water pushes the grains of sand apart, leaving a pool of liquid. This makes buildings constructed on swampy ground particularly likely to collapse during an earthquake. When an earthquake struck the Loma Prieta district of San Francisco in 1989, buildings standing on a site that had

HIGHLIGHTS

◆ Earthquakes are shock waves caused by movement within Earth's crust.

◆ Most earthquakes occur along fault lines where breaks occur in Earth's crust.

◆ The strength of an earthquake is measured by seismometers, instruments that record the size of shock waves.

◆ The strength of earthquakes can be measured by several scales, including the Richter scale.

The earthquake in Mexico City in 1985 measured 8.1 on the Richter scale and caused much damage.

across the ocean at speeds of 300 to 400 miles per hour (480 to 640 km/h). When they reach shallow coastal waters, they grow in size to tower 50 feet (15 m) or more in the air. As the tsunamis crash against the shore, they often cause enormous damage. Low-lying areas such as Hawaii, Alaska, and Japan have been pounded by tsunamis many times.

Fires are another major hazard after an earthquake. They often break out because electricity or gas supply lines have been ripped apart. After the 1906 San Francisco earthquake, fires started by damaged gas mains destroyed more than 28,000 buildings. The fires raged for three days because the city's water mains had also been cut. Firefighters finally managed to control the blaze by dynamiting a wide avenue in the city center to create a firebreak.

Earthquakes occur most often along plate boundaries. The world's largest and most active earthquake zone is around the rim of the Pacific plate, the portion of Earth's crust that bears the Pacific Ocean. This rim is called the Ring of Fire because volcanic eruptions are also common there. The west coasts of North and South America, the Aleutian Islands, Japan, the Philippines, New Zealand, and many South Pacific islands are all located on the so-called Ring of Fire. About 80 percent of the world's earthquakes happen there.

North America's most notorious fault line is the San Andreas Fault in California, on the Ring of Fire. It runs along the West Coast of the United States for 750 miles (1,210 km), from the Imperial Valley on the Mexican border north as far as Cape Mendocino. The fault has been the source of some of the world's most devastating earthquakes, including the Fort Tejon quake of 1857 and the San Francisco earthquake of 1906. Many scientists believe southern California is in line for another big earthquake, at some time in the 21st century.

The Alpine zone is a second major earthquake belt. It begins in the Azores (a group of islands off the coast of Portugal) and runs through the Mediterranean Sea, Turkey, Iran, and northern India, down to Sumatra, Indonesia, and New Guinea. In 1999, two devastating quakes hit Turkey in the Alpine zone.

once been a lagoon suffered heavy damage, while many built on firmer ground remained intact.

When an earthquake strikes a coastal region or out to sea, the shock waves sometimes cause giant waves called tsunamis (soo-NAH-meez) to form. Tsunamis can race for thousands of miles

Underwater, the most active earthquake belt is the Mid-Atlantic Ridge. This submerged mountain chain runs the length of the Atlantic Ocean and reaches the surface in Iceland, the Azores, Ascension, and other Atlantic islands.

Five percent of earthquakes occur far from plate boundaries. Most U.S. states have had at least one in the last 300 years, yet only the West Coast lies along a plate boundary. Seismologists (syz-MAH-luh-jists), scientists who study earthquakes, understand little about these quakes.

Measuring earthquakes

Seismologists use sensitive instruments called seismometers (syz-MAH-muh-tuhrz) to measure the strength of earthquakes. Seismometers record both the size and pattern of seismic waves. By comparing readings from seismometers in different locations, scientists are able to pinpoint the exact location of the earthquake's epicenter.

EVERYDAY SCIENCE

Monitoring Earthquakes

The town of Golden, Colorado, holds a quiet room filled with buttons, gauges, and giant paper-covered rollers where earthquake experts watch over Earth. Mechanical pens rest against a dozen huge rolls of graph paper. The rolls represent 12 seismology stations located throughout the United States. Other machines stand ready to receive information from 3,000 similar stations around the globe.

This is the headquarters of the National Earthquake Information Service. When an earthquake strikes anywhere in the world, an alarm bell rings. Computer printers chatter as data from hundreds of earthquake stations flood in. High-speed computers analyze the information to find out the earthquake's strength and location. Within an hour, the center has supplied details of the quake to the government, relief services, and the media.

Most of the time, work at the center is less dramatic, but just as important. Workers analyze data from thousands of smaller tremors. This information helps scientists to understand more about Earth, and seismologists to pinpoint the danger areas where future quakes may strike.

This road has been split in two by an earthquake.

Various scales are used to define an earthquake's intensity. The Richter scale, invented by U.S. seismologist Charles Richter (1900–1985) in 1935, is the most commonly used. There is no upper limit to the Richter scale, but the scale usually ranges from 0 to 9. The difference of just one number means that the vibrations are 10 times stronger. Earthquakes that measure between 6.0 and 6.9 on the Richter scale are considered moderate, but they can still be disastrous in highly populated areas. Most major quakes measure 7.0 to 7.9.

To measure the destructive power of an earthquake, the Mercalli scale is used. Devised in 1931, this scale has 12 levels of intensity and relies on eyewitness observations of the quake. The moment-magnitude scale is a precise new scale that uses exact measurements made at the fault before and after the quake.

LOOK CLOSER

Major Earthquakes

The most powerful earthquake ever recorded in the United States measured 8.5 on the Richter scale. It struck Alaska on March 27, 1964, causing 131 deaths and damage estimated at $750 million. An even more powerful quake is thought to have hit New Madrid, Missouri, in 1811, but there is no data to prove it. According to stories, the earthquake rang church bells in Boston, toppled chimneys in Cincinnati, and woke President James Madison from his sleep at the White House in Washington, D.C.

The famous San Francisco earthquake of 1906 is estimated to have measured 8.3 on the Richter scale. This figure is based on the damage caused. The quake killed at least 315 people; another 352 were never accounted for. City buildings were destroyed over an area of 5 square miles (13 sq km), mainly by the fires that broke out in the wake of the earthquake.

A massive quake hit Chile in South America in 1960. Measuring 8.5 on the Richter scale, it killed 5,000 people and destroyed more than 400,000 homes. In 1985, the Michoacan earthquake killed 10,000 people and toppled 7,000 buildings in Mexico City. The quake began on the Mexican coast 250 miles (400 km) away. Damage in the capital was made worse because much of the city is built on a dried-up lake bed. When the quake struck, the partly hollow lake bed behaved like a drum, bouncing with each tremor.

The quake that struck the city of Kobe in Japan in 1995 measured only 6.8 on the Richter scale, but it caused great damage in this heavily populated area. Nearly 5,500 people died, and the damage was estimated at $110 billion.

In 1999, northwest Turkey was rocked by two major earthquakes. The first struck in August and measured 7.4 on the Richter scale. It was one of the largest earthquakes of the 20th century. It killed thousands of people, injured tens of thousands more, and caused damage estimated at $40 billion. The second quake, in November, was slightly smaller but still killed hundreds and injured thousands in the Turkish mining town of Duzce.

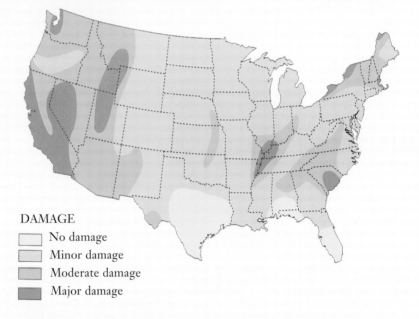

DAMAGE
- ☐ No damage
- ☐ Minor damage
- ☐ Moderate damage
- ☐ Major damage

This seismic map of the United States shows the areas where the maximum destruction could occur in an earthquake.

Predicting earthquakes

Several earthquakes were successfully predicted in the 1960s and 1970s. In 1975, seismologists in China predicted from a series of minor tremors that a major earthquake would hit the city of Haicheng within 24 hours. The quake duly hit within the deadline.

One of the best ways to predict earthquakes is to study the patterns of previous earthquakes in a region. Evidence is found in the rocks that lie along the fault. Recently, seismologists have turned away from earthquake prediction to concentrate on trying to minimize the effects of quakes. Most earthquake deaths and damage are caused by the collapse of buildings. Scientists are now perfecting ways to make buildings better able to withstand the violent shaking of the ground that occurs during a major earthquake.

CHECK THESE OUT!
✔EARTH ✔FAULT ✔OCEAN
✔PLATE TECTONICS ✔VOLCANO

Eclipse

When light from the Sun or other star is hidden by another celestial body

One of the most exciting astronomical events to be seen from Earth is an eclipse (ih-KLIPS). Eclipses yield new information about the Sun, Moon, planets, and even the distant stars.

Eclipses occur when something passes in front of a shining object, blocking the light from it. For example, when someone passes their hand between their eye and a shining light bulb, the light is blocked from reaching their eyes. The bulb is in eclipse.

Solar eclipses

Various eclipses occur in space. Eclipses of the Sun (solar eclipses) are the most dramatic. They occur when the Moon comes between Earth and the Sun, so Earth lies in the Moon's shadow. An eclipse can be either total or partial. During a total solar eclipse, the centers of the Sun, Moon, and Earth form a straight line in space. During a partial eclipse, the three planets are not in a perfectly straight line, so only part of the Sun is hidden by the Moon.

During a total solar eclipse, the Moon covers the Sun's disk completely. This happens because of an extraordinary coincidence: the Sun is 400 times larger than the Moon, but it is also 400 times farther away from Earth than the Moon.

A solar eclipse showing the diamond ring effect.

This makes the Moon and the Sun appear exactly the same size from Earth. However, both Earth's orbit around the Sun and the Moon's orbit around Earth are not perfect circles. This means that sometimes the Moon does not completely cover the Sun. When this happens a ring of sunlight is seen around the black disk of the Moon. This is called an annular eclipse.

How often do solar eclipses happen?

When the Moon lies between, but not directly between, Earth and the Sun, only the side of the Moon facing away from Earth is lit up. The Moon is invisible to watchers on Earth. This effect is called the new moon. A new moon occurs about once a month, so one might expect to see a total solar eclipse as often. However, the Moon does not orbit Earth in exactly the same plane as Earth orbits the Sun. Therefore solar eclipses occur much less often than new moons.

HIGHLIGHTS

- An eclipse happens when the light of one celestial body is hidden by another.

- Solar eclipses occur when the Moon comes between Earth and the Sun.

- Lunar eclipses happen when Earth is between the Sun and the Moon.

Two to five partial solar eclipses occur each year. Total solar eclipses happen once every one or two years. During a solar eclipse, the shadow of the Moon follows a narrow track across Earth. The area within which the total eclipse can be seen is called the zone of totality. As the eclipse begins, the air temperature cools. The light dims when the Moon blocks the Sun, then darkness falls for a period of around two minutes. Animals may begin to behave as they do at dusk. Sometimes sunlight appears above the Moon, and this is called the diamond ring effect. Soon the Sun appears again on the opposite side of the Moon's disk, and the sunlight and warmth return.

Scientists observe solar eclipses in order to study structures of the Sun that protrude beyond the Moon's covering disk. These include the corona, the top layer of the Sun's atmosphere. Normally, these structures would be impossible to study as they are lost in the glare of the Sun.

Lunar eclipses

An eclipse of the Moon happens when Earth comes between the Sun and the Moon. The disk of Earth casts a shadow that covers the Moon either partially or completely. The Moon takes on a brown or coppery-red color as its light is refracted (bent) through Earth's atmosphere. Lunar eclipses occur only when the Moon is full. They happen less frequently than solar eclipses.

Total solar eclipses are visible only within a small area on the surface of Earth.

Eclipses and discoveries

The Sun, Moon, and Earth are not the only celestial bodies involved in eclipses. Other planets can be eclipsed by their own moons. Stars can be eclipsed, too, in a process called an occultation (AH-kuhl-TAY-shuhn).

In 1977, an occultation led to an unexpected discovery. A group of astronomers were about to view the planet Uranus gradually sliding in front of a distant star. They expected the light of the star to wink out suddenly. Instead they saw a series of blinks. Something near Uranus had repeatedly blocked and unblocked the light streaming toward Earth. Later, when the star appeared on the other side of the planet, the blinking was repeated. The scientists suspected that the blinking was caused by a series of rings circling Uranus. This theory was confirmed when the space probe *Voyager 2* discovered 11 rings around the planet in 1986.

During the 17th century, astronomers observed the peculiar behavior of certain stars. They seemed to grow dimmer and brighter at regular intervals. The riddle was solved by English astronomer Sir William Herschel (1738–1822), helped by the work of his sister Caroline Herschel (1750–1848). He suggested that the stars were double (binary) stars, orbiting each other. As these stars eclipse one another, so their combined light fades then brightens.

CHECK THESE OUT!
✔BINARY STAR ✔LIGHT ✔MOON ✔SUN

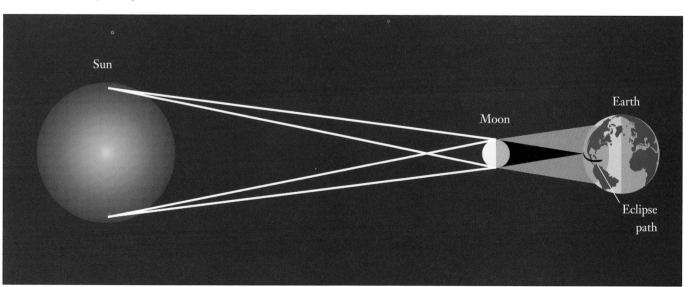

Sun

Moon

Earth

Eclipse path

Elasticity

The ability of materials to return to their original form after being deformed

The stretchiness or elasticity of everyday materials is a very important property. From the rubber soles of sneakers to the metal springs that absorb shocks in cars, all kinds of everyday items need to bend and stretch repeatedly without breaking. A spring is a good example of an object that is elastic. It can be stretched by some distance, but if the stretching force is released, the spring returns immediately to its original length. Elasticity is one of the most important things that engineers and architects must consider in the design of buildings and structures.

Hooke's law

An elastic object such as a metal spring can be stretched very easily. Doubling the force doubles the amount by which the spring stretches, and releasing the force returns the spring to its original length. This effect was first noted by English scientist Robert Hooke (1635–1703) and is called Hooke's law. Another way of describing

A bungee jumper applies the force of his weight to test the elasticity of the bungee rope.

the effect is to say that the amount of stretch is proportional to (varies with) the stretching force.

However, even the strongest spring can be stretched only so far. The spring eventually reaches a point called the elastic limit. Any stretching beyond this point permanently stretches the spring, so it will no longer return to its original length. Beyond the elastic limit, the spring stretches much more easily. This is called plastic deformation, because a very small force now causes a considerable amount of stretching, and the spring is permanently changed or deformed. Eventually the spring breaks completely at a certain maximum limit called the yield point.

Describing elasticity

Different terms are used to describe how elastic materials behave when forces are applied to them. The stress on an object is defined as the total force divided by the area over which it is applied. Suppose a bungee jumper tries out two different ropes, one of which is twice as thick as the other. The force (the bungee jumper's

HIGHLIGHTS

- An elastic object changes shape when a force is applied to it, then it returns to its original shape when the force is removed.

- Hooke's law says that doubling the force applied to an object doubles the amount by which it changes shape.

- Stress is the force acting on the object divided by the area over which it is applied.

- Strain is a measure of how much the object changes shape, compared to its original shape, when it is under stress.

The amount a spring stretches varies proportionately with the amount of force applied to it. So a spring might stretch by ⅖ inch (1 cm) with a 1-kg (2-pound) weight, and by ⅘ inch (2 cm) with a 2-kg (4-pound) weight.

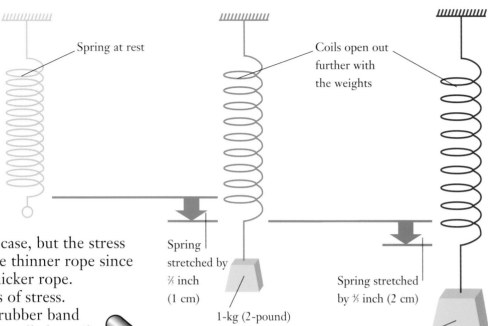

Spring at rest

Coils open out further with the weights

Spring stretched by ⅖ inch (1 cm)

1-kg (2-pound) weight

Spring stretched by ⅘ inch (2 cm)

2-kg (4-pound) weight

weight) is the same in each case, but the stress will be twice as much on the thinner rope since it has half the area of the thicker rope.

There are different kinds of stress. Pulling an object such as a rubber band so that its length increases is called tensile (TEN-suhl) stress. Pushing or squeezing an object so it becomes shorter is called compressive stress, and it works just the same way as tensile stress according to Hooke's law. If the compressive stress is removed, the object returns to its original length.

Strain is a measure of how much an elastic body has stretched. Strain is defined as the change in length of an object divided by its original length. So for a metal spring, the more it is pulled, the greater its length and the greater the strain it is under. For any one material, dividing the stress by the strain always gives the same number, which is called the elastic modulus. Materials such as steel have a high elastic modulus. This means they withstand a great deal of stress with much less strain. They do not stretch much even when a large force is applied.

Designing for elasticity

Engineers and architects have to bear in mind the elasticity of the materials they use. Bridges have to be designed to withstand the stresses and strains of heavy traffic, as well as buffeting by the wind. Skyscrapers are constructed from a framework of steel girders, which must support all the weight of a building and its occupants. By carefully designing the structure so that some of the girders are in compression and some in tension, it is possible for architects to ensure that the weight of a building is distributed evenly. No

LOOK CLOSER

Stretchy Rubber

The elasticity of a material depends on the way its atoms and molecules move when a force is applied. Strong solid materials, such as metals, have their atoms tightly packed in a regular structure. It is impossible to move one atom without moving all the others. This tight packaging makes metals strong. Elastic solids such as rubber are made from long chains of molecules. Applying the same force to a piece of rubber and a piece of steel causes much more stretching in the rubber because it is easier to straighten the long molecular chains in the rubber than to move the tightly packed atoms in the steel.

single girder has to bear a force that would stretch it dangerously beyond its elastic limit.

Different materials behave in different ways when they are stressed and strained many times. Iron can stretch almost any number of times within its elastic limit. Other metals gradually weaken. This is called fatigue (fuh-TEEG), and it is important in aircraft manufacture.

CHECK THESE OUT!
✔FORCE ✔MATTER

Electricity

Events in which electric charges move or are gathered together in one place

Flashes of lightning and electric trains, digital watches and electric eels, robot dogs, and cellular phones are just a few examples of how electricity is experienced in the everyday world. Physicists divide the study of electrical events into two distinct parts: static electricity (electrostatics) and current electricity. Static electricity deals with electric charges that build up and remain in one place. Current electricity deals with electric charges that move from one place to another.

Electricity may seem to be a modern discovery, but its effects have been known since the time of the ancient Greeks. Now that these effects are better understood, electricity is used not only to transmit power but as a means of storing and transmitting information in devices such as telephones, satellites, and computers.

Principles of electricity

If someone walks up and down repeatedly across a nylon carpet, their hair may start to tingle and they may feel themself building up a static charge. This is an example of electrostatics. If they then touch a metal object,

HIGHLIGHTS

- Until the end of the 18th century, scientists knew about only static electricity.

- The connection between electricity and magnetism was first established in 1820.

- J. J. Thomson's discovery of the electron in 1897 helped scientists understand why some materials are conductors (carry an electric current and have low resistance) while others are insulators (carry a current poorly or not at all and have high resistance).

- Direct current (DC) flows steadily in one direction; alternating current (AC) rapidly and repeatedly changes direction.

such as a doorknob or faucet, they may get quite an electric shock because the charge flows rapidly to Earth, through the person, as an electric current. The movement of electric charge is a good example of current electricity.

Most electrical events result from the motion of tiny particles inside atoms called electrons. Each electron carries a tiny negative charge. If the number of electrons in one place is greater than the positive charge on the nuclei of the atoms in the same place, an overall negative charge is formed. Similarly, if there are too few electrons there is a lack of negative charge, or a positive charge. When electrons move from one place to another, an electric current is created.

To make a current flow without interruption, there must be a complete path around which the electrons can travel. This path is called a circuit (SUHR-kuht). The current that flows when a lamp is switched on is made of billions of electrons moving together. If the current always moves in the same direction, it is called a direct current (DC). It is easy to produce a current that switches back and forth. Such currents are called alternating currents (AC). Alternating currents are a more efficient way of supplying power to the home than direct currents.

The structure of some materials, such as the metals copper and gold, makes it very easy for electrons to flow through them. For this reason, they carry electric currents very easily and are called

conductors. Materials that do not conduct electricity as well, such as glass and rubber, are called insulators (IN-suh-lay-tuhrz). They can be used to protect (or insulate) people from the harmful effects of dangerous electric currents. For this reason, high-voltage electric cables are often coated in thick rubber. Materials that conduct well are said to have high electrical conductance; those that conduct poorly are said to have a high electrical resistance. Conductance and resistance are the opposite of one another.

History of electricity

Static electricity has been known since the time of the ancient Greeks (around 600 B.C.E.). During the 17th and 18th centuries C.E., physicists believed electricity was caused by an electric fluid that could build up in one place or flow from one place to another. This idea is not so very different from the modern theory that static electricity is caused by an accumulation of electrons, and current electricity by a flow of electrons from one place to another.

Although static electricity has a long history, current electricity has only been understood more recently. It was first investigated in a series of experiments by Italian anatomy professor Luigi Galvani (1737–1798). He found that if he dissected (dih-SEKT-uhd; cut off) a frog's leg and hung it on a brass hook that was itself

Entire cities rely on electricity as a source of power. This can be seen by the bright lights of these office blocks in Sydney, Australia.

André Marie Ampère, the French physicist for whom a unit of electric current (amp) is named.

If electric currents could produce magnetic fields, could magnetic fields also produce electric currents? English chemist Michael Faraday (1791–1867) found that a current will flow through a piece of wire if it is moved through a magnetic field. His experiment meant turning a large copper disk between the poles of a magnet. As the disk turned, a current flowed through it. Faraday's method of using mechanical energy (physically turning the copper disk) to produce electrical energy (the current) marked the discovery of the electric generator, a device for producing electricity. Electric generators are now used to produce the world's electricity.

Electricity and magnetism seemed to be very closely related, but it was not until 1864 that their relationship was properly understood. Scottish physicist James Clerk Maxwell (1831–1879) worked out a set of four equations (now called Maxwell's equations) that explain

attached to an iron railing, the frog's leg twitched when it accidentally touched the iron. Although Galvani believed this was caused by animal electricity inside the leg, the real cause was an electric current that flowed when the two different metals were connected in a circuit. This discovery was made by another Italian, physicist Alessandro Volta (1745–1827). In 1799, Volta showed that combinations of different metals separated by cardboard soaked in saltwater could be used to generate electricity. This invention, the Voltaic pile, was the world's first battery.

During the 19th century, a number of scientists discovered that electricity was very closely related to magnetism. In 1820, Danish physicist Hans Christian Ørsted (1777–1851) found that switching on an electric current would cause the needle of a nearby compass to rotate. This happens because an electric current produces a magnetic field (the lines of force that radiate out from a magnet). Some years later, French physicist and mathematician André Marie Ampère (1775–1836) found different ways in which wires carrying currents could generate magnetic fields. He also devised a way to measure the effect. Electric current is now measured in units called amperes (AM-PIRZ), or amps, in honor of his achievement.

DISCOVERERS

Edison, Swan, and the Electric Light

Early electric lights invented in the 19th century consisted of two graphite (GRA-fyt; soft carbon) rods held a short distance away from one another. When a high voltage was connected between the rods, a continuous spark leapt in an arc from one rod to the other. Although these early arc lights were widely used in many public buildings, they were very bright, very smelly, and the rods quickly wore out and had to be replaced.

U.S. inventor Thomas Alva Edison (1847–1931) is popularly remembered as the inventor of the electric light bulb. English inventor Joseph Wilson Swan (1828–1914) also played a part, however. Edison came up with a lamp design in 1879. It consisted of a carbon filament (thin wire) inside a glass bulb from which the air had been sucked out. When a current passed through the filament, it glowed. Joseph Swan came up with a similar design at the same time. After a dispute over who owned the invention, the two men joined forces and formed the Edison and Swan United Electric Light Company in 1883 to manufacture light bulbs. Modern light bulbs are similar to these, but contain filaments made from the metal tungsten.

LOOK CLOSER

How Materials Conduct Electricity

A metal solid, such as a piece of copper, is made of layers of copper atoms closely packed together into a multistory grid called a lattice. The atoms are bonded (held) together by their outer electrons, which can move freely throughout the lattice. Electrons carry negative charge, so the moving electrons in a metal allow it to carry a current and conduct electricity. In other solids, such as rubbers and plastics, there are no free outer electrons floating through the structure. All the electrons are involved in a type of bonding that keeps them in the area between individual pairs of atoms. As the electrons do not move readily, there is nothing to carry a current. This explains why insulators do not readily conduct electricity. Insulators have a very high resistance because they resist the passage of a current.

In a conductor not connected to a power source, the electrons move randomly about with a speed that depends on the temperature. Once an electric field is set up in the conductor, the electrons experience a force causing their random motion to favor one direction over the others. Such a field is set up when the conductor is connected across the terminals of a battery. One of the earliest batteries, of the type invented by Alessandro Volta, is shown here. It is also called a Voltaic pile, since it is made of identical cells piled on top of each other. The ability of a battery to set up an electric field in conductors is called its electromotive force, and it is measured in volts, after Volta.

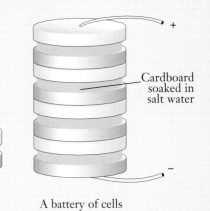

Silver
Zinc
One cell

Cardboard soaked in salt water

A battery of cells

how electricity and magnetism give rise to one another. Another piece of the puzzle was completed in 1897 when J. J. Thomson (1856–1940), discovered the electron and confirmed that it carried electric currents.

Using electricity

Today, electricity is probably familiar to most people not as lightning bolts or flowing electrons but as a clean and convenient source of power carried direct to their homes. Electric generators change energy from a variety of different forms into electrical energy. The energy of a dammed river is a mixture of potential energy (which the water has because of its height) and kinetic energy (which the water has because of its movement). In a hydroelectric power plant, this energy is used to turn a huge wheel with fins called a turbine (TUHR-byn), which is attached to a generator that produces electricity as it rotates. In a coal-fired power plant, burning coal produces high-pressure steam. This steam is funneled through a steam turbine that extracts the heat from the steam and uses it to turn a

generator in much the same way. Solar electric plants can produce electricity directly from sunlight using devices called photocells (FOH-toh-selz). Photocells are made from materials such as silicon. They produce an electric current automatically whenever light shines on them.

Power plants are often a long way from the homes and factories they supply. Once electricity has been generated, it must be shipped long distances. The cables used are so long that significant power losses occur, even if good conductors are chosen for the wires. In practice, the losses are reduced by transmitting electricity at very high voltages. Devices called transformers increase the voltage produced at the power plant. Electricity is carried through thick cables supported by metal towers called pylons before other transformers reduce (step down) the voltage near homes and factories.

CHECK THESE OUT!
✔BATTERY ✔CATHODE RAY ✔COPPER
✔ELECTROMAGNETISM ✔ELECTRON ✔ELECTRONICS
✔ELECTROSTATICS ✔ENERGY ✔SEMICONDUCTOR

Electrolysis

The use of an electrical current to cause a chemical change in a compound

The general name for a process that uses an electrical current to cause chemical changes is electrolysis (ih-lek-TRAH-luh-suhs). This process is the opposite of how a battery works. Batteries produce an electrical current as chemical changes happen in the substances inside them. Perhaps the most familiar example of electrolysis takes place in rechargeable batteries. When the chemical reaction in a battery is complete, a charging current reverses the reaction by electrolysis and the battery can then be reused.

Electrolytic cells

Electrolysis takes place in electrolytic cells (ih-lek-trah-LIH-tik SELZ). These cells have one positive and one negative electrode in a conducting liquid. A direct current (DC) power supply causes current to flow in one direction only. The conducting liquid (electrolyte) is often a solution of a salt in water. When salts dissolve, their positive and negative ions become free to move separately. When the cell is connected to the electrical source, positive ions in the solution drift toward the negative electrode, and negative ions drift toward the positive electrode. This is a result of the attraction between opposite charges.

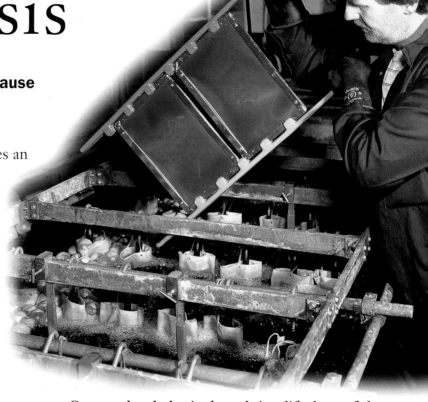

Copper-plated plastic sheets being lifted out of the bath in which they have been electroplated.

In some electrolytic cells, the conducting liquid is a molten salt at high temperature. Molten salts are used when water would interfere with the electrolytic process. Often the heat that makes the salt melt comes from the electrical current, just as an electric heater becomes hot when current flows through it.

Other types of cells

In one type of electrolytic cell, the electrodes are inert (ih-NUHRT; they play no part in the chemical reaction but provide the current for it to happen). Industrial cells that produce caustic soda (sodium hydroxide, NaOH) are an example of this type of cell.

Brine, a solution of common salt in water, is the starting material for these cells. When common salt (sodium chloride, NaCl) dissolves in water, it splits into sodium ions (Na^+) and chloride ions (Cl^-). Water contains hydrogen ions (H^+) and hydroxide ions (OH^-).

When the current is switched on, both hydrogen ions and sodium ions move toward the negative electrode (the cathode). The hydrogen

HIGHLIGHTS

◆ An electrolyte is the dissolved or molten substance through which an electrical current is conducted.

◆ Electroplating is a form of electrolysis that coats objects with copper, gold, silver, and tin.

◆ Many useful materials for the chemical industry come from electrolytic processes.

ions have a greater attraction for electrons than do the sodium ions, so the hydrogen ions pick up electrons first. As they do so, they lose their positive charge and pair up to form hydrogen molecules (H_2). Bubbles of hydrogen gas form at the cathode:

$$2H^+ + 2e^- \text{ (from cathode)} \rightarrow H_2$$

At the positive electrode (the anode), chloride ions (Cl^-) and hydroxide ions (OH^-) from water compete to give up their electrons. Chloride ions win, and bubbles of chlorine form at the anode:

$$2Cl^- \rightarrow Cl_2 + 2e^-$$

This reaction continues until there are no more hydrogen or chloride ions. A solution of sodium hydroxide in water remains. All three products—chlorine, hydrogen, and sodium hydroxide—are useful industrial chemicals.

Electroplating cells

In another type of cell, the electrodes themselves take part in the reaction. One example is the type of cell used for electroplating (see below). A similar cell is used to purify copper. Impure copper is the positive electrode in this cell and pure copper is the negative electrode. The electrolyte is copper sulfate. When the current is switched on, copper ions move through the solution and coat the pure copper cathode. At the same time, the impure copper anode dissolves as it gradually feeds the plating reaction. The impurities, which include gold and silver, drop to the floor of the tank.

CHECK THESE OUT!
✔CHEMICAL REACTION ✔ELECTRICITY ✔ELECTRON

LOOK CLOSER

The Electroplating Process

Solid silver cutlery is prized for its attractive appearance. Unfortunately, it is also very expensive. A cheaper substitute can be made by coating steel cutlery with a thin layer of silver (see diagram). Objects are electroplated by placing them in a bath that contains a solution of a salt of the coating metal (the electrolyte). The salt used for silver plating is silver cyanide, one of the few silver salts that dissolves in water. The object to be coated, such as a spoon, is the negative terminal of the plating bath. A bar of coating metal, in this case silver, is the positive terminal. When the current is switched on, positive metal ions drift toward the negative charge of the object that is being coated. When the metal ions reach the spoon, they pick up electrons and become metal atoms. The metal atoms can no longer dissolve in water and form a film of silver on the surface of the spoon. While the current flows, the DC source takes in electrons from the positive electrode, which is the bar of coating metal. These electrons come from metal atoms as they become positive metal ions and go into solution. The bar of coating metal becomes smaller as it dissolves and has to be replaced from time to time.

Electroplating is the ideal process for coating metal articles because it produces an even film of metal over the surface in the solution. The thickness of the film depends on the strength of the electrical current and the coating time. The coating process can therefore be controlled easily. Gold, chromium, copper, and tin are other common coating metals. Alloys such as brass and bronze can be coated onto objects by using mixtures of metal salts in the coating bath. Electroplating can also coat the surfaces of materials that do not conduct electricity, such as plastics and wood, by spraying them with a conducting coating before they go into the coating bath.

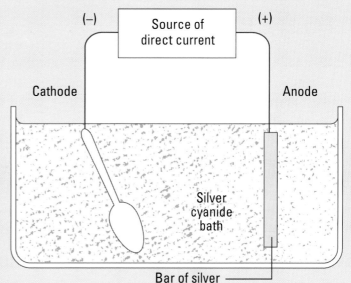

Electromagnetic Spectrum

The complete range of electromagnetic radiations, including visible light

When light from the Sun passes through a wedge-shaped piece of glass called a prism (PRIH-zuhm), it splits into a rainbow of different colors called a spectrum. This spectrum includes red, orange, yellow, green, blue, and violet. However, red and violet are not the real ends of the spectrum. Sunlight contains other types of radiation, similar to light but invisible to human eyes. These radiations, including visible light, are all part of the electromagnetic spectrum.

Light waves and color

Light is made of continuous waves following each other, just like ripples in water. Each wave has a wavelength, which is the distance between the peak of one wave and the peak of the next wave. Each wave also has a frequency, which is a measure of the number of separate waves that go past a certain point in one second, measured in cycles per second (Hertz, symbol Hz). For example, a water wave might have a wavelength of 2 inches (5 cm) and a frequency of 2 Hz. The peaks of the wave are 2 inches (5 cm) apart, and two waves go past a fixed point every second. The wavelength multiplied by the frequency gives the wave's velocity (vuh-LAH-suh-tee; speed). In one second any point on this wave will have moved forward by 4 inches (10 cm), so its velocity is 4 inches per second (10 cm/s).

Early in the 20th century, physicists discovered that light has a constant speed of 186,282 miles per second (299,792 km/s) through empty space. As in the case of the water wave, the wavelength multiplied by the frequency of any light wave must equal the wave velocity for that frequency. As the wavelength gets longer, its frequency must decrease, and as the frequency increases, the wavelength must get shorter.

The speed of light is always constant in a vacuum (VA-kyoom; empty space), but it is reduced when light travels through a material such as glass or water. The different wavelengths of light are slowed down by different amounts in a material such as glass, which is why a prism splits light into the different colors.

The broader spectrum

The human eye can detect colors from red, with wavelengths around 770 nanometers (nm), to violet, with wavelengths around 390 nm (1 nm is a billionth of a meter). Around 1800, British astronomer Sir William Herschel (1738–1822) discovered the Sun was emitting an invisible type

HIGHLIGHTS

- The different radiations in the spectrum have different wavelengths and frequencies but all travel at the same speed through empty space—the speed of light.

- Apart from visible light, the first electromagnetic radiations to be discovered were infrared and ultraviolet (UV).

- The full spectrum contains very long radio waves, infrared, visible light, ultraviolet, X rays, and very short, high-energy gamma rays.

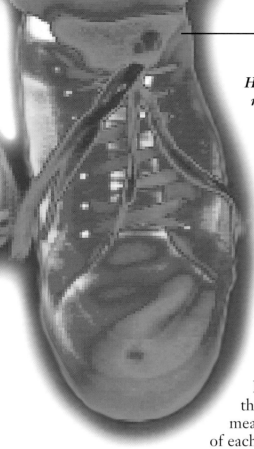

Heat (infrared radiation) given off by feet in sneakers is shown as different colors. Red areas are the warmest.

of radiation with longer wavelengths than red light. He had split sunlight using a prism. He used a thermometer to measure the heat of each color. When he found the temperature started to rise past the red end of the spectrum, he had discovered infrared radiation.

Another type of invisible radiation was soon discovered. German physicist Johann Wilhelm Ritter (1776–1810) found that silver chloride, a chemical that darkens when exposed to light and is used widely in photography, also darkened when exposed to radiation from beyond the violet end of the spectrum. He had found ultraviolet (UV) light.

Discovering electromagnetic waves

The discovery of these new types of radiations helped scientists who were trying to understand exactly what light was. Everyone recognized it was a wave of some sort, but no one understood what type of wave it was or how it was able to travel through a vacuum. All waves need a medium (substance that helps it travel), such as water for a water wave or air for a sound wave.

In the early 1800s, English physicist Michael Faraday (1791–1867) was experimenting with electricity. He discovered that an electric current passing through a wire could generate a magnetic field around it and that a moving magnetic field could generate an electric current in a wire. He suggested this might be how light waves worked.

If light waves contained both an electric and a magnetic wave, the two parts would continually reinforce each other, allowing the waves to travel for vast distances without getting smaller.

Scottish scientist James Clerk Maxwell (1831–1879) proved Faraday's idea. The resulting theory (idea) showed that electromagnetic waves perfectly matched the behavior of light, infrared, and ultraviolet radiations.

The mystery of how light is transmitted through a vacuum was not solved until the early 20th century with the arrival of the theory of relativity and quantum theory, important laws of physics. However, Maxwell's theory made important predictions that could eventually be proved. It accurately described the entire range of the electromagnetic spectrum, from radio waves, through infrared, visible, and ultraviolet light, to X rays and gamma rays.

Radio waves

In 1888, German physicist Heinrich Hertz (1857–1894) proved Maxwell's theories with a clever experiment that was to change the world. Hertz placed two pairs of metal rods on opposite

---

EVERYDAY SCIENCE

Fluorescence

One useful effect of ultraviolet light is called fluorescence (floo-REH-suhnts; glowing). When ultraviolet light strikes some materials, the atoms absorb it and temporarily gain a little energy. This energy gain changes the electrons' motion within the atoms. They soon settle back into a lower energy level, but in steps, each step releasing some of the energy as radiation. The radiation released has a lower frequency, a longer wavelength, and falls inside the visible part of the spectrum. Therefore the material glows visibly when ultraviolet light shines on it. Fluorescence can be used to detect substances without the need for complex chemical analysis. When ultraviolet light is shone on food, for example, fluorescence shows if contaminating bacteria are present. Similarly, fluorescence by UV light is used to study the paints present in suspected forged paintings and to identify genuine banknotes.

sides of his laboratory. Hertz passed an electric current through one pair (the transmitter) and created a spark across the tiny gap between the rods. He found a smaller spark was created between the other pair, which was acting as the receiver. The signal spark was making an electromagnetic wave that was being picked up at the receiver and changed back into electricity.

Hertz had discovered radio waves, which have the longest wavelengths in the electromagnetic spectrum. The shortest radio waves are around 1 mm long, and there is no upper limit to their length. The radio end of the spectrum extends forever. Because radio waves have long wavelengths, they also have low frequencies. This means they carry little energy and can be created quite easily. Their long wavelength also allows them to pass through and around smaller obstacles without being affected. This ability has allowed radio waves to change the world. Without them, radio, television, and satellite communications would be impossible.

Radio waves with the shortest wavelengths, called microwaves, are small enough to be absorbed. Microwaves have wavelengths of about 1 mm. They can make atoms in materials vibrate violently, heating them up. In a microwave oven, microwaves are absorbed by the water and fat in food, which become hot and heat the rest of the food.

Infrared

Infrared radiation covers the part of the spectrum between radio waves and visible light, that is, wavelengths ranging from 1 mm to around 800 nm. It is created by the movement of individual atoms and molecules. Because this movement increases when a material gets hotter, hotter objects emit more infrared radiation. Infrared is sometimes called heat radiation. If an object such as an iron bar is heated enough, then the radiation it gives out will move from the infrared into the visible, from red heat to white, and eventually to blue, as the atoms inside the iron bar vibrate with more and more energy.

Visible light

Human eyes can detect radiation with wavelengths between around 770 nm (deep red) and 390 nm (deep violet). Most objects on Earth do not produce light but instead reflect it. Humans see the particular colors that are reflected by an object. Visible light is unusual because it is one of the few radiations that can pass through Earth's atmosphere without being absorbed. Atoms in the atmosphere absorb nearly all of the electromagnetic spectrum. The only wavelengths that can get through the atmosphere are in narrow windows. One of these windows covers long radio waves, and another covers the region around visible light. Most radio and infrared radiation, and nearly all the wavelengths shorter than visible light, are blocked by the atmosphere. Many of these radiations, such as ultraviolet and X rays, are harmful to life.

Ultraviolet

Beyond the violet end of visible light, ultraviolet radiation has wavelengths between around 400 nm and 5 nm. Just as visible light is emitted by objects hotter than infrared, ultraviolet is emitted by even hotter objects. Although the Sun radiates mostly infrared and visible light, it also produces lots of ultraviolet, which is blocked by ozone (OH-zohn; a bluish, very reactive gas) in the upper atmosphere. It is possible to heat some objects until they emit most of their radiation in the ultraviolet. Ultraviolet light is more easily made using a discharge tube, which is a glass tube filled with atoms of xenon or mercury gases at low

A flower that is plain yellow in sunlight shows dark streaks and patches under ultraviolet light.

LOOK CLOSER

Wavelength and Frequency

This diagram shows the wavelengths in empty space and the frequencies of different radiations. The wavelengths in air are almost the same. There are no real boundaries between different types of radiation in the spectrum. This is why the wavelength ranges for many of the different radiations overlap. For example, the shortest ultraviolet rays have the same properties as the longest X rays. As the wavelength of each type of electromagnetic wave lengthens, its frequency gets lower because the frequency multiplied by the wavelength always has to equal the speed of light, 186,282 miles per second (299,792 km/s) in a vacuum. Often the longest waves (radio waves) are described by their frequencies, and the shortest by their wavelengths. This is why a radio is tuned to a frequency rather than a wavelength.

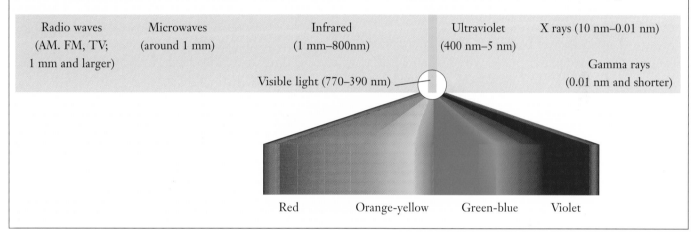

Radio waves (AM. FM, TV; 1 mm and larger)

Microwaves (around 1 mm)

Infrared (1 mm–800nm)

Ultraviolet (400 nm–5 nm)

X rays (10 nm–0.01 nm)

Gamma rays (0.01 nm and shorter)

Visible light (770–390 nm)

Red   Orange-yellow   Green-blue   Violet

pressure. When a sufficiently high-voltage electric current is applied to the tube, electrons are pulled away from some of the gas atoms and accelerated (made to speed up). When these high-speed electrons collide with other gas atoms, they transfer some of their energy to them. When the atoms return to their normal state, they release ultraviolet light.

X rays

With wavelengths between 10 nm and 0.01 nm, X rays have even higher energies than ultraviolet light. Some stars are hot enough to produce X rays. On Earth, X rays are produced by the collision of electrons with atoms, usually in a metal target sealed inside a discharge tube.

X rays were discovered by German physicist Wilhelm Röntgen (1845–1923) in 1895. Because they have very high energies, X rays penetrate and sometimes pass straight through soft materials. The X-ray photographs that doctors take to see inside the human body use photographic film to contrast areas where the X rays pass straight through soft tissue and areas

where the X rays are absorbed by hard bone or denser organs. The shapes of bones are particularly easy to see on an X ray.

Gamma rays

Electromagnetic waves with the shortest wavelengths (shorter than 0.01 nm) are called gamma rays. They are released by radioactive materials. When a radioactive atom splits into two smaller atoms, it releases energy as a gamma ray. Astronomers now know that some gamma rays reach Earth from space and others are formed as cosmic rays strike Earth's atmosphere.

Gamma rays have such high energies that they can penetrate most materials. Only thick sheets of lead or other dense materials will stop them. Gamma rays can destroy living cells. Under controlled conditions, gamma rays can be used to kill bacteria so as to sterilize medical instruments or increase the shelf life of food.

CHECK THESE OUT!

✔COSMIC RAYS ✔ELECTROMAGNETISM ✔QUANTUM THEORY ✔RADIO WAVE ✔SPECTROSCOPY

Electromagnetism

The force behind both magnetic and electric phenomena

The first signs of a link between electricity and magnetism (now known to be aspects of the same force, called electromagnetism) were discovered in the 1820s. The invention of batteries had made it easy to generate electric currents, and scientists began to experiment with electricity for the first time. In 1820, Danish scientist Hans Christian Ørsted (1777–1851) discovered that an electric current flowing through a wire made a nearby compass needle move. In the same year, French physicist André-Marie Ampère (1775–1836) discovered that two parallel (straight, side-by-side) wires with currents flowing in them could act like magnets. If the currents through the wires ran in the same direction, the wires were attracted to each other. If the currents ran in opposite directions, the wires repelled each other.

Ampère went on to discover a law showing that the strength of the magnetic field around a wire increased if the current through it increased, and decreased with distance from the wire. However, he could not explain where the magnetism came from.

Faraday's electromagnetic field

The idea that electricity and magnetism were closely related was first put forward by English scientist Michael Faraday (1791–1867). Faraday carried out a series of experiments that completely changed the theories of electricity and magnetism and paved the way for many of the inventions on which modern life relies.

Faraday's greatest breakthrough was to discover the shape of the magnetic fields produced around a wire. Everything else developed from this discovery. Faraday arranged a vertical wire so it passed through a horizontal sheet of paper. Then he scattered iron filings onto the paper. When he ran a current through the wire, he found that the filings arranged themselves in a circular pattern around the wire. Almost everyone had thought that the magnetic field from the wire would consist of rays running straight out from it. Faraday's experiment showed that the magnetic field acted at right angles to the current and curved, like the field around a magnet.

These discoveries led Faraday to invent the idea of a field of force. This is still the easiest way to understand how electricity and magnetism work. An electric or magnetic field is drawn as a series of curving lines with arrows on them. These lines show the direction of the force that would affect an electric charge or magnet pole

The electromagnet picks up some metal objects as the current is turned on, and then drops them once the current is turned off.

HIGHLIGHTS

♦ An electric current can create a magnetic field, and a changing magnetic field can create an electric current.

♦ Michael Faraday put forward the idea of electric and magnetic fields, and James Clerk Maxwell proved they are aspects of a single force.

♦ Electromagnets are very strong magnets made by placing a rod of iron or other magnetic material in an electric coil.

♦ Generators change mechanical movement into electrical energy, and motors change electrical energy into mechanical movement.

placed in the field at that point.

The idea of fields of force was adopted by Scottish mathematician James Clerk Maxwell (1831–1879). He used it to prove mathematically that electrical and magnetic fields were aspects of the same thing, and he created the idea of a combined electromagnetic force.

Electromagnetic induction

Faraday's discovery of how electric currents and magnetic fields were related led him to another very important discovery. Just as an electric current can create a magnetic field, so a magnetic field can generate an electric current. When Faraday passed a bar magnet in and out of a wire coil, he found that a current flowed through the wire.

Faraday took his discovery one step further and showed that as an electric current can create a magnetic field, and a magnetic field can create an electric

current, it is possible to create a current in a wire just by putting it close to another wire with a current already passing through it. Faraday called this effect electromagnetic induction.

One way of demonstrating electromagnetic induction was to wind two coils around opposite sides of an iron ring. Faraday connected one of these coils to a galvanometer (a meter that measures current), and the other to a battery. He found that when the battery was connected, the galvanometer needle flickered briefly. When the battery was disconnected, the needle flickered again. The induced current always flowed in the opposite direction to the flow from the battery, and it flowed only when the magnetic field around the wires was changing.

Today it is known that induction happens because the changing magnetic field pushes around current-carrying electrons inside the wire. The force that acts on the electrons is called the electromotive force (EMF).

DISCOVERERS

James Clerk Maxwell (1831–1879)

James Clerk Maxwell took the results of Faraday's experiments, which suggested that electricity and magnetism were related, and gave them a mathematical grounding. He discovered that electrical and magnetic fields were transmitted by electromagnetic waves traveling at the speed of light. Visible light is just one example of an electromagnetic wave. Maxwell's discovery led to the development of radio and television.

Electromagnets

A huge range of modern machines rely on the principles of electromagnetism and induction discovered by Faraday and Maxwell, such as electromagnets, transformers, generators, and motors. Most are based on just a few basic principles. Probably the simplest device that uses Faraday's discoveries is the electromagnet, a strong magnet created by multiplying the magnetic field created inside a coil.

Electromagnets were

discovered in 1825 by British physicist William Sturgeon (1783–1850), when he placed an iron rod inside a magnetic coil. He found that the field created by the coil was amplified (increased) by the natural magnetic particles in the iron, turning the rod into a powerful bar magnet.

Electromagnets are more useful than normal permanent magnets because their magnetism can be switched on and off simply by controlling the electric current through their coils. Also, the larger the current running through the coil, the more powerful the magnet becomes. Electromagnets can generate much stronger magnetic fields than permanent ones.

Modern electromagnets may have iron cores or cores of an alloy (metal mixture) or compound of several elements. Because some electrical conductors lose all electrical resistance at very low temperatures, it is possible to make strong superconducting electromagnets that require no power source once the current has been established. These strong magnets are often used in magnetic resonance imaging (MRI) machines that make it possible for physicians to see inside the human body without using X rays.

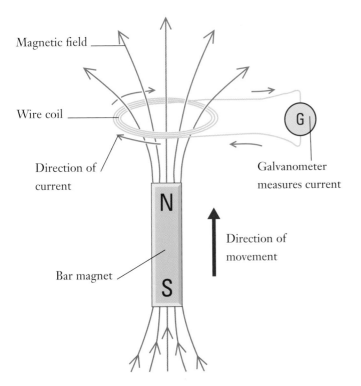

Magnetic field

Wire coil

Direction of current

Galvanometer measures current

N

S

Direction of movement

Bar magnet

As the bar magnet moves toward the wire coil, it induces a current in the wire coil.

Transformers

While studying induction, Faraday found that the current induced in the secondary coil depended on the number of turns of wire in each coil. If the secondary coil contained twice as many turns as the primary, then the induced current would be half the original current. The electric voltage induced in the coil, however, would be doubled. This principle is used today in transformers, which change the voltage of a power supply. By using alternating current (AC), which is constantly changing, the magnetic field in the transformer can also be made constantly to change, inducing an alternating current in the secondary coil.

Step-up transformers, with more turns in the secondary coil than in the primary, are used to create high voltages and low currents, which are ideal for transmitting electricity over long distances along cables. Step-down transformers can return the supply to the lower voltage and higher current needed in homes.

Generators and motors

Generators and motors use electromagnetism to transform movement into electrical energy, and electrical energy back into movement. An electric generator usually has a coil rotating (turning) between the poles of a magnet or electromagnet. As the coil rotates, it changes its position with respect to the magnetic field, and an alternating current is induced in it. The mechanical power that makes the magnets spin usually comes from turbines (engines) spun by water or steam.

A motor is basically a generator in reverse. An electric current running through the coil, which can be turned, experiences a twisting force, or torque (TORK). The connection between the coil and the power supply is set up so the current direction changes when needed to keep the torque always in one direction.

Faraday discovered the principle of the electric motor in 1831, but modern alternating current motors are based on the induction motor designed by Croatian-born U.S. engineer Nikola Tesla (1856–1943) in 1883.

CHECK THESE OUT!
✔ELECTRICITY ✔ELECTRON ✔MAGNETISM

Electron

Negatively charged particle that is the smallest particle in an atom

The electron is the smallest particle of matter. An electron has a tiny mass and a negative electrical charge. Electrons carry the electrical charge in an electrical current, and they are involved in forming the chemical bonds that hold atoms together in particular groups called molecules (MAH-lih-KYOOLZ).

Discovery of the electron

In the 19th century, scientists and engineers made many electrical devices without knowing exactly what happens when an electrical current flows. One such device was the cathode-ray tube, which was invented in the 1870s by British physicist Sir William Crookes (1832–1919).

A cathode-ray tube is a sealed glass tube that contains gas at a very low pressure. A wire called a cathode is at one end of the tube. The opposite end of the tube is coated on the inside with tiny crystals called phosphors (FAHS-fuhrz). When the cathode is connected to the negative terminal of an electrical source, the phosphor-coated screen glows. If an object is placed in the tube between the cathode and the screen, the object casts a shadow on the screen. Cathode rays got their name because they form shadows in a similar way to rays of light.

In 1897, British physicist J. J. Thomson (above) proved that cathode rays were composed of negatively charged particles (named electrons). He received the Nobel Prize in physics in 1906.

In 1897, British physicist J. J. Thomson (1856–1940) was studying the effect of electric and magnetic fields on cathode rays. An electric field produces a force on objects that carry an electrical charge. If a current flows through a wire, the wire produces a magnetic field that can be attracted or repelled by a magnetic field surrounding the wire. When Thomson saw that electric and magnetic fields caused cathode rays to bend, it occurred to him that he was observing a current of charged particles flowing through a vacuum (VA-kyoom; empty space) rather than through a wire.

By varying the fields, he calculated the ratio of the particles' charge to their mass. He found this ratio to be almost 2,000 times the same ratio for a hydrogen ion (H^+). Guessing that the charge would be the same size as the charge of a hydrogen ion, Thomson suggested that the particles in cathode rays had a mass almost one-two thousandth the mass of a hydrogen ion.

HIGHLIGHTS

◆ The electron is the smallest particle of matter.

◆ An electron has a very small mass and a tiny negative charge.

◆ The mass of an electron is approximately one-two thousandth the mass of a proton.

◆ Electrons behave as waves or as particles.

EVERYDAY SCIENCE

The Positron

In the early 20th century, scientists were working to find equations that would describe how atoms and other minute particles behave. British physicist Paul Dirac (1902–1984) produced equations that describe how electrons move. The same equations predicted that another particle, the positron, should exist. In 1928, Dirac suggested that the positron would be identical to the electron in all properties apart from its charge. The charge would be equal and opposite to the charge of an electron. In 1932, U.S. physicist Carl Anderson (1905–1991) found evidence of positrons as he was observing the behavior of cosmic rays. Cosmic rays are fast-moving, charged particles that arrive in Earth's atmosphere from outer space. They are studied in devices called cloud chambers, where they leave traces of condensation as they pass through water vapor. Because cosmic rays are charged particles, electric and magnetic fields can bend their paths. When Anderson detected a particle that was deflected in the wrong direction for an electron, he knew he had discovered the positron. Anderson won a share in the 1936 Nobel Prize for physics for this discovery.

Since the discovery of positrons in cosmic rays, scientists have found various sources of positrons on Earth. For example, some radioactive isotopes produce positrons when they decay. Even common elements, such as carbon, oxygen, nitrogen, and fluorine, have positron-emitting isotopes (variations in the atoms of an element) that can be made in nuclear reactors.

Positrons are an example of antimatter, or antiparticles of electrons. If an electron collides with a positron, the two particles destroy each other and produce a burst of energy. The energy takes the form of two gamma rays, which are high-energy photons.

Positron-emission tomography (PET) uses positrons to study the flow of blood in organs such as the brain. A radiologist injects a small amount of a positron-emitting substance into the bloodstream of a patient. Each time a positron is formed, it self-destructs as soon as it meets an electron. Detectors around the patient pick up the pair of gamma rays and the source of the gamma rays can be traced by geometrical calculations. A computer maps the positions of several positron emissions to produce a three-dimensional image of the flow of blood. PET images help in the diagnosis of tumors (TYOO-muhrz; abnormal lumps of body tissue) and study of brain activity.

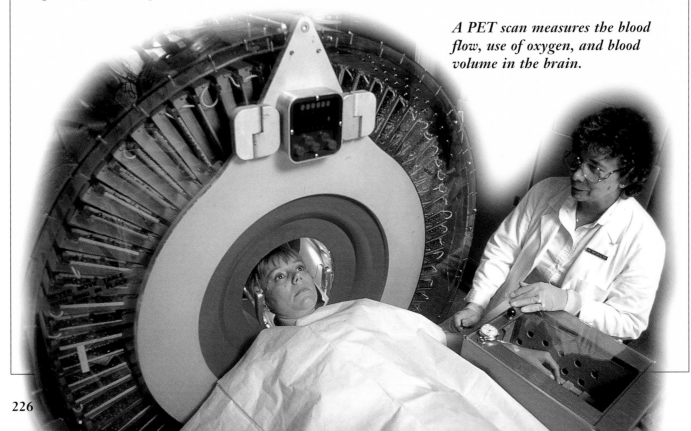

A PET scan measures the blood flow, use of oxygen, and blood volume in the brain.

The charge of an electron

Thomson's results gave only the ratio of an electron's charge to its mass. They did not give exact values for either the mass or the charge of an electron. Nevertheless, Thomson was convinced that electrons were tiny fragments of atoms. Other scientists disagreed and thought instead that atoms were the smallest possible pieces of matter. The idea that atoms could be split into even smaller parts was difficult to accept.

This view changed with the work of U.S. physicist Robert Millikan (1868–1953). Millikan's plan was to measure the charge of individual electrons. In 1913, Millikan performed a number of experiments with droplets of oil. He sprayed oil into a chamber and let the spray fall between two metal plates that could be connected to an electrical source. The upper plate had a negative charge, and the lower plate had a positive charge. A beam of X rays knocked one or more electrons out of some of the oil drops, leaving them with positive charges. Millikan watched the oil drops through a magnifying lens as they fell between the plates. By measuring how fast they fell without the electrical supply turned on, he could calculate their weight. He would then connect the power. The negative charge on the upper plate would attract the positively charged drops. At a certain voltage, this attraction would stop an oil drop from falling from the upper plate to the lower plate.

From this voltage and the weight of the drops, Millikan was able to calculate the size of the charge carried by the oil drops. After several measurements, he found the charge was always a multiple of the same value: 1.6×10^{-19} coulombs. Millikan's value for the charge of the electron is very close to measurements made today with modern precision instruments.

Millikan published his results in 1914, stating that this value was the charge of the electron. Because he had confirmed the charge of an electron to be the same value that Thomson had suspected, Millikan was also able to confirm that electrons were tiny fragments of atoms.

Using a device called a bubble chamber, physicists can observe the paths of moving electrons. Patterns of electron activity are shown in this photograph.

A particle or a wave?

In 1905, German-born U.S. physicist Albert Einstein (1879–1955) put forward the idea that light consists of tiny packets of energy. He based his theory on experimental results that could not be explained by light being a simple wave. These packets of energy, which he called quanta (KWAHN-tuh), behaved as particles. In 1924, French physicist Prince Louis de Broglie (BROH-lee; 1892–1987) suggested that if light waves could act as particles, electron particles might also behave as waves.

A series of experiments with electron beams in 1927 confirmed this theory. If electrons were particles, then a beam of electrons fired at a narrow slot would simply continue as a straight beam after the slot. However, it was observed that electron beams spread out after passing through a narrow slot, in the same way that sound waves spread around corners and through doorways. By the 1930s, electron beams were being used instead of light beams for high-magnification microscopes.

Electrons in atoms

In 1911, Ernest Rutherford (1871–1937), a British physicist at Manchester University in England, suggested that atoms were mainly empty space around a tiny core called the nucleus

This scientist studies an insect's leg using a scanning electron microscope installed in the University of California at Berkeley.

(NOO-klee-uhs) that contained almost all their mass. He based this theory on the results of experiments where he had fired tiny particles, called alpha (AL-fuh) particles, at a gold foil (FOY-uhl; very thin metal sheet). Most of the particles passed through the foil. Only a few bounced back after hitting a nucleus inside an atom of gold. Between 1913 and 1915, Niels Bohr (1885–1962), a young theoretical physicist from Denmark, took this idea further by suggesting that the electrons of an atom moved in a series of orbits in the empty space around an atom's nucleus, in the same way that moons orbit a planet.

In 1926, Austrian physicist Erwin Schrödinger (1887–1961) combined de Broglie's notion of wavelike electrons with Bohr's model. Schrödinger believed that instead of being particles in orbit, electrons behaved as if they were waves trapped around a nucleus. He produced equations that described their motion and calculated the shapes of these trapped waves. Schrödinger's equations were one of the foundations of quantum mechanics, a theory that changed the way that physicists view the nature of matter and energy.

CHECK THESE OUT!
✔CATHODE RAY ✔ELECTRICITY ✔ELECTROMAGNETIC SPECTRUM ✔QUANTUM THEORY

LOOK CLOSER
The Electron Microscope

Microscopes use light to produce images of objects too small to be seen clearly with the naked eye. Photons (FOH-tahnz; bundles of light) bounce off or shine through an object under the microscope. Lenses in the microscope focus the light into images that can be seen with the naked eye.

The power of a microscope is called its resolving power. This is related to the distance there must be between two objects for the microscope to produce separate images of them. If the gap between two objects is similar to the size of a photon, a light microscope will see them as a single blurred image. Light microscopes can magnify to a maximum of around 2,000 times because of this effect.

Electron microscopes use beams of electrons to produce images. An electric field speeds up electrons because it attracts negatively charged electrons from a negative metal plate to a positive plate. At high speeds, electrons behave like waves with very short wavelengths. A typical electron microscope might accelerate electrons through 60,000 volts. The wavelength of electrons at this voltage is 0.005 nanometers (nm; one-billionth of a meter) compared with 390 to 770 nm for visible light. Since electrons at this speed have wavelengths around one-one hundred thousandth those of visible light, they can provide images of objects 100,000 times smaller than the limit for light microscopes. The electrons' wavelength gets shorter as the voltage increases.

Objects can be magnified up to one million times with the best electron microscopes. The space inside the microscope has to be under vacuum, since air would block the electron beam. Glass lenses would also block electrons, so electron microscopes use electric and magnetic fields to focus the beam. In transmission electron microscopes, the electron beam passes through the sample and forms a two-dimensional image on a fluorescent (glowing) screen. Crystals on the back of the screen glow when struck by the beam. In scanning electron microscopes, a beam traces across the surface of the sample and is reflected onto a screen. A three-dimensional image builds up as the beam scans across the sample.

Electronics

Using the flow of electrons around a circuit to control machines and to store and process information

The 21st century world of information and communications depends very largely on electronics. This is the technology by which tiny charged particles called electrons are used to control electrical devices, such as microwave ovens, and to store or process information, such as in calculators and computers. The basic science on which electronics is based has been understood for over a century. During that time, scientists have gained a better understanding of electronics and how to apply it. This knowledge has made electronic devices smaller and less expensive. It is now possible to make a wide variety of miniature electronic devices, such as digital watches and cellular phones, that would have been unthinkable 50 years ago.

How electronics works

Electrical devices are operated by applying a voltage so that an electric current passes through them. A current flowing through a lamp makes the filament (FIH-luh-muhnt; thin wire) heat up and give off light. There is nothing especially

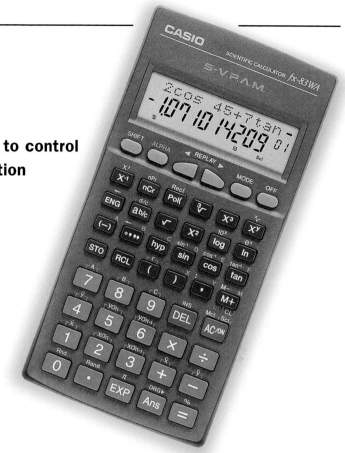

Calculators use electrons to store and process information.

clever about an ordinary electric current. It does not carry information or control the lamp beyond simply switching it on or off. The current that flows in electronic devices is much more sophisticated. In a radio, for example, the signal transmitted by a distant broadcasting station is captured by the antenna (an-TEH-nuh; a device for receiving radio waves), transformed (changed) into an electrical current, and amplified (made louder) into a sound that can be heard. In a computer, a flow of current is used to store numbers, carry out calculations, and operate equipment such as an industrial robot. The key difference between electrical and electronic equipment is whether the current provides power to the device (as in electrical equipment), or controls the device or carries information (as in electronic equipment).

Electronic devices can be built in a variety of ways, but they are usually made out of standard building blocks called electronic components (parts). These parts are linked together to form a circuit (SUHR-kuht) that carries out a specific task. Different circuits are needed for different

HIGHLIGHTS

♦ Electronic equipment is made from components such as resistors, transistors, and capacitors.

♦ In electrical equipment, an electric current simply supplies power. In electronic equipment, the electric current controls and carries information.

♦ Electronics developed after the discovery of the electron by J. J. Thomson in 1897.

♦ Three main inventions have been responsible for the modern electronic revolution: the vacuum tube, the transistor, and the integrated circuit.

tasks. There is a number of types of electronic components, such as resistors (rih-ZIS-tuhrz), capacitors (kuh-PA-suh-tuhrz), diodes (DY-OHDZ), and transistors (tran-ZIS-tuhrz). Resistors oppose the flow of a current and can be used to make different amounts of current flow through different parts of a circuit. Capacitors store electric charge and are often used in timing circuits. Diodes allow current to flow in one direction only. Some types of diodes called LEDs (light-emitting diodes) are often seen on stereos or scientific instruments in the form of small colored indicator lights. Transistors can amplify a current (make it larger) or switch it on and off. By putting these components together in different ways, it is possible to build a huge variety of different electronic devices. Radios, televisions, and computers are built of components such as these.

Electronics in action

It is hard to think of an area of modern life that does not depend on electronic equipment. Devices that were once mechanical or electrical are now, often, electronically controlled. For example, many homes have a

microwave oven. These machines use electronic timing circuits to switch on and off microwave-generating devices according to the type and weight of the food being cooked.

Some electronic devices contain sensors wired into circuits that can trigger alarms if certain things happen. Smoke alarms constantly check the air around them and set off an alarm if they detect smoke particles. In hospitals, electronic monitoring equipment checks a patient's heart rate and blood pressure and triggers an alarm if they should reach dangerous levels.

Apart from monitoring and control, electronic equipment is also used for storing and processing information. Information on a computer screen and numbers on a calculator are both converted (changed) into electronic signals flowing around tiny circuits. All the information processed by computers is transformed into long strings of zeros and ones (called binary numbers; BY-nuh-ree), which computers can process more efficiently than the decimal numbers people use.

History of electronics

During the 19th century, German and British physicists carried out a number of experiments that involved putting a high voltage across two

Electronic circuit boards have uses in a variety of electronic products.

LOOK CLOSER

Digital Electronics and Binary Code

Early electronic devices such as the triode valve simply increased or decreased the strength of a tiny electrical current. This process is called analog (A-nuhl-ahg) electronics because the current can be of any value. Computers and other information-processing devices use digital electronics, in which a current can take one of only two values: it either flows or it does not. A current is used to represent the number 1; the absence of a current is used to represent the number 0. Computers can represent any decimal number (or any letter or graphical symbol) by turning the number into a long string of zeroes and ones, which is called binary code.

An electrical current travels in pulses through the integrated circuit of this computer chip.

electrical terminals (called electrodes) at either end of a long glass tube full of different types of gases. As a result, an electric current flowed between the two electrodes, which could be used to generate light if it were directed onto a phosphorescent (FAHS-fuh-RES-suhnt; glowing) screen. This discovery eventually led to the invention of television, radar sets, and other similar devices. The research also led British physicist J. J. Thomson (1856–1940) to discover a tiny, negatively charged particle called the electron in 1897. Electronics developed as a result of his remarkable discovery.

The cathode-ray tubes used in these experiments were changed into a device called a diode valve or vacuum (VA-kyoom) tube diode. This small glass bulb contained a positive terminal (anode or positive electrode) and a negative terminal (cathode or negative electrode) heated by a wire filament. Its inventor, British electrical engineer John Ambrose Fleming (1849–1945), found the device would allow a current of electrons to flow in only one direction (just like the mechanical valve in a water pump), even if the connections were reversed.

A new type of vacuum tube was invented by U.S. engineer Lee de Forest (1873–1961). Called a triode, it had three electrodes and could amplify electrical currents. It was used in early radio sets to boost the strength of weak signals.

Electronic vacuum tubes were completely new, but they were also expensive and unreliable. Early computers built from vacuum tubes were constantly breaking down. Fortunately, in 1947, three U.S. physicists named John Bardeen (1908–1991), Walter Brattain (1902–1987), and William Shockley (1910–1989) invented a much more reliable electronic component called the transistor. Transistors amplified currents just like a vacuum tube but could also switch currents on and off and so enable computers to make simple decisions. Further, since they did not need a heated filament, they could be used without the warm-up time needed with vacuum tubes.

In the 1950s, Jack Kilby (born 1923) of Texas Instruments and Robert Noyce (1927–1990) of Fairchild Semiconductor found a way to package hundreds of electronic components onto a tiny slice of silicon. Called an integrated circuit, the device evolved in 1971 into a tiny chip containing all the components needed to make a computer. This device was called a microchip, silicon chip, or more properly a microprocessor. Microprocessors are now used in almost every piece of modern electronic equipment, from microwave ovens to cellular telephones.

CHECK THESE OUT!

✔CATHODE RAY ✔ELECTRICITY ✔ELECTRON
✔LIQUID CRYSTAL ✔SEMICONDUCTOR

Electrostatics

The study of the effects of electric charges at rest

A variety of phenomena (fih-NAH-muh-nuh; facts or events) that take place when electrical charges build up in one place are called electrostatics. A good example of electrostatics is lightning. Sometimes the effects of electrostatics are unpredictable and unwanted. For example, when a person walks across a nylon carpet in sneakers and then touches a doorknob, they may get an electric shock. On a much larger scale, lightning happens when positive and negative charges are separated in a thundercloud and the electrical effects become strong enough to break down surrounding air. Electrostatics can also be extremely useful, however. Its various uses include painting automobiles on a production line and spraying crops from an aircraft.

The negative electrostatic charge from this Van de Graaff generator passes to the boy's hair and makes it stand on end.

HIGHLIGHTS

- There are two types of electric charge, positive and negative. Adding electrons to an object makes it negatively charged; removing electrons makes it positively charged.

- Electrostatic principles are used in crop and paint spraying, in smokestacks to prevent pollution, and in office copying machines.

- Electrostatic events have been known since the time of the ancient Greeks (around 600 B.C.E.).

- When too much charge builds up in one place, the surrounding air will break down, resulting in a spark or lightning.

How electrostatics works

Suppose a Perspex rod is rubbed with a woolen cloth and then suspended from a nylon thread. If a second Perspex rod is rubbed and held near the first one, the suspended rod begins to swing away from the rod being held. The two rods repel (push away from) one another. Now suppose a polyethylene rod is rubbed and brought up to the suspended Perspex rod. Instead of repelling, as the two Perspex rods did, the Perspex and polyethylene rods attract one another.

The theory of electrostatics explains why this happens. When a Perspex rod is rubbed with a woolen cloth, electrons (the tiny negatively charged particles that move around inside atoms) flow from the rod to the cloth. There are now too many electrons in the cloth, which makes it negatively charged, and too few electrons in the Perspex rod, which makes it positively charged. When a second Perspex rod is brought alongside the first one, the two rods are both positively charged. The two rods move away from one another because like charges (charges that are the same kind, positive or negative) repel. Something different happens when a polyethylene rod is rubbed. Electrons now flow from the cloth to the rod. These extra electrons make the rod negatively charged and the cloth positively charged. When the negatively charged polyethylene rod is brought up to the positively charged Perspex rod, the two rods move toward one another because unlike charges (charges that are different) attract.

History of electrostatics

The effects of electrostatics have been known since the time of the ancient Greeks. Around 600 B.C.E., Greek philosopher Thales of Miletus (around 624–around 547 B.C.E.) found that when he rubbed amber (a hard yellow resin) with a cloth, it would build up a charge and be able to pick up feathers or straw. In 1600 English physician William Gilbert (1544–1603) found that substances other than amber produce an attractive force when rubbed. He called that force electrical because the Greek word for amber was *elektron*.

In 1714, French physicist Charles Du Fay (1698–1739) found that rubbing different substances sometimes caused an attractive force and sometimes a repulsive force. He believed that the two different forces were caused by two kinds of electrical fluid that would flow between objects when they were rubbed together. In 1750, U.S. scientist and statesman Benjamin Franklin (1706–1790) suggested a different theory. He believed there was only one kind of electrical fluid. Too much of this produced one kind of electrical force, whereas too little produced the opposite kind of force. Franklin's theory is very similar to the modern understanding of electrostatics, in which different effects are produced by objects having either too many or too few electrons.

Electrostatics in action

Electrostatics is very helpful in everyday life. The spray guns used on an automobile production line give the paint a small electrical charge, which helps to distribute the paint evenly to all parts of the car bodies. A similar idea is used by aircraft that spray crops with pesticides. The spray is given an electrical charge as it is released, and this ensures that the pesticide is

LOOK CLOSER — Van de Graaff Generator

A Van de Graaff generator, named for its inventor, U.S. physicist Robert Van de Graaff (1901–1967), is a machine for producing large amounts of electrostatic charge. It has three main parts: a power supply connected to a needle point at the bottom, a large metal sphere connected to a needle point at the top, and a conveyor belt made of an insulating material running between the two. The needle point at the bottom sprays charge onto the belt, while that at the top allows it to escape from the belt and spread over the sphere. (In some simpler machines, including those used in science classrooms, a simple motor is used to turn the belt, and the charge is generated by friction only.) Gradually, a massive charge builds up on the metal sphere, with a voltage of up to eight million volts.

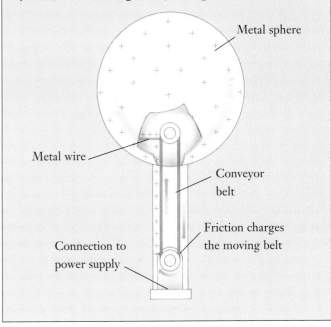

Metal sphere

Metal wire

Conveyor belt

Friction charges the moving belt

Connection to power supply

attracted to both the tops and bottoms of the leaves. Power station smokestacks sometimes have electrically charged grids at the top, which are used to help remove particles of ash and dirt and so reduce air pollution.

CHECK THESE OUT!

✔ELECTRICITY ✔ELECTROMAGNETISM
✔ELECTRON ✔ELECTRONICS

Element

A substance consisting entirely of atoms that have the same atomic number

An element is a substance in which all atoms have the same atomic number, that is, the number of protons (positively charged particles) in the nucleus (NOO-klee-uhs). There are 90 naturally occurring elements. Scientists have also manufactured 20 more. Uncombined elements are rare in nature, since most elements are very reactive and are more stable (unreactive) in a compound (combined with one or more other elements). The few exceptions include gold, helium, and oxygen and nitrogen in the air.

Atoms

Atoms are the smallest particles of an element. They contain three types of smaller particles, called subatomic particles, namely electrons, neutrons, and protons. The nucleus of an atom is a clump of neutrons and protons. These two types of particles have very similar masses. Protons have a positive electrical charge, while neutrons have no charge at all.

A cloud of electrons surrounds the nucleus. The mass of an electron is around one-two thousandth of the mass of a neutron or proton. Each electron has a negative charge that matches the positive charge of a proton. An atom, which

Most scientists believe that all the elements on Earth were formed in the stars.

overall has no electrical charge, contains the same number of electrons and protons. The electrons move rapidly around the nucleus in a set of orbits (each called a shell) that is around 10,000 times the width of the nucleus. If a nucleus were the size of a soccerball, the width of the electron cloud would be ½ mile (800 m).

Elements can be put into groups and laid out as a table called the periodic table. The elements in a group tend to behave in similar ways chemically. How an atom behaves in chemical reactions depends on the arrangement of its electrons into shells, especially the outermost shell. This shell can fill up with a certain number of electrons. The elements with a nearly empty

---

HIGHLIGHTS

◆ Elements are made of small particles called atoms, which are in turn made of electrons, neutrons, and protons.

◆ There are 90 natural elements on Earth, and scientists have made about 20 artificial elements.

◆ Except for hydrogen and the artificial ones, the elements are formed by fusion in stars.

or a nearly full outermost shell are the most reactive. Elements with a nearly empty outermost shell easily lose one or more electrons to become positively charged. An example is sodium (Na), which becomes Na^+. Those with a nearly full outermost shell easily gain one or more electrons to become negatively charged. An example is chlorine (Cl), which becomes Cl^-.

Nuclear structure

The simplest nucleus is that of the hydrogen atom, which is a single proton with no neutrons. All other types of nuclei (NOO-klee-EYE) have neutrons as well as protons. They are held together by an attraction called the strong force. In a stable nucleus, the strong force is powerful enough to hold together the nucleus against the strong repulsion between like-charged protons. Neutrons help to dilute the positive charge in the nucleus. This is why the heavier elements have a larger number of neutrons than protons.

In almost all cases, there is more than one type of nucleus for a given element. Different forms, called isotopes (EYE-suh-tohps), have different numbers of neutrons. All isotopes of uranium, for example, have 92 protons, but the number of neutrons varies between 130 and 150.

Elements from stars

All the elements on Earth, apart from hydrogen and artificial ones, came from stars. In a star, fragments of nuclei move around at enormous speeds and extreme pressures. Under these conditions, the fragments collide and sometimes stick to each other to form larger nuclei. This process is called fusion (FYOO-zhuhn).

CHECK THESE OUT!
✔ATOM ✔COMPOUND ✔PERIODIC TABLE

LOOK CLOSER

New Elements and the Island of Stability

The Berkeley Laboratory of the University of California has discovered many new elements, 18 elements between 1936 and 1999. Technetium and astatine fill gaps among the naturally occurring elements. The other new elements are called transuranic elements because they have atomic numbers greater than uranium.

To make these elements, the Berkeley team used a device called a cyclotron (SY-kluh-trahn) to accelerate atomic nuclei to very high speeds. These nuclei are fired at target nuclei in a device called a collider. In most cases, two colliding nuclei bounce off each other. In some cases, however, the force of the collision is strong enough for the strong force to take over and pull the nuclei together to form a single, larger nucleus. In many cases, these elements exist for only fractions of a second.

For years, many scientists believed that 106 was the greatest possible atomic number. Some scientists predicted there would be combinations of neutrons and protons that could form nuclei with an atomic number of around 116. They called this the island of stability because it formed a patch on the graph of atomic numbers and numbers of neutrons. In 1999, the Berkeley team confirmed the island of stability by making two new elements with atomic numbers 116 and 118.

Name	Atomic number	Year of discovery
Technetium	43	1936
Astatine	85	1940
Neptunium	93	1940
Plutonium	94	1940
Americium	95	1944
Curium	96	1944
Berkelium	97	1949
Californium	98	1950
Einsteinium	99	1952
Fermium	100	1952
Mendelevium	101	1955
Nobelium	102	1958
Lawrencium	103	1961
Rutherfordium	104	1969
Hahnium	105	1970
Seaborgium	106	1974
Element 116	116	1999
Element 118	118	1999

El Niño and La Niña

Seasonal air and ocean currents in the Pacific that affect the weather worldwide

The seasonal air and ocean currents that disrupt weather patterns in the Pacific Ocean are called El Niño and La Niña. They bring changes in the atmosphere that affect the weather worldwide. Torrential rainfall, flooding, drought (DRAOOT; excessive dryness), and famine (FA-muhn; extreme lack of food) can result when these currents are unusually strong. These times are called El Niño or La Niña events or years.

Warm ocean currents: El Niño

The waters of the eastern Pacific Ocean along the coast of Peru are relatively cool, but they support many tropical fish and birds. This abundance is linked to El Niño, a warm ocean current that flows southward along the coast between December and March each year. Every three to seven years, however, this current begins early, flows more strongly, and lasts longer. When this happens, the local weather changes. Heavy rains fall on the normally dry coast of Peru. Plants and animals from inland rain forest areas arrive to colonize the coast.

HIGHLIGHTS

◆ El Niño is a warm Pacific Ocean current that flows south along the coast of Peru in winter.

◆ In some years El Niño is unusually strong, disrupting weather patterns around the world.

◆ El Niño brings torrential rain and flooding to some regions; in other areas, it brings drought.

◆ La Niña is another seasonal air and ocean current system in the Pacific, producing weather changes broadly opposite to those caused by El Niño.

Local fishers knew of the warm current as early as the 19th century. Since it usually appears in early December, they named it El Niño, meaning "the boy" in Spanish, referring to the baby Jesus.

El Niño causes life to flourish on land but it shuts off deep, cooler waters that usually well up in the ocean. These nutrient-rich waters usually support huge numbers of plantlike and animal plankton (tiny organisms), which in turn provide food for larger sea creatures, such as fish. When El Niño flows more strongly than usual, the cool waters fail to well up, and fish such as anchovies move away. The failure of the anchovy harvest off Peru was one of the first signs of the destructive power of El Niño.

El Niño affects the winds

Scientists studying El Niño knew that the warm ocean current affected the oceans off Peru and thus the fish, seabirds, and other aquatic creatures of the region. They soon began to realize that the warm sea current was also affecting the air above the oceans and thus the prevailing winds.

Normally, air rises above the western Pacific, flows eastward at great heights, then descends over the eastern Pacific. At lower altitudes, powerful winds called trade winds blow in the opposite direction. These winds flow westward from an area of high pressure over the eastern Pacific toward an area of low pressure near Indonesia. They pull some of the cool water away from the South American coast. This pattern is disturbed when El Niño flows unusually strongly.

El Niño is linked to a disruption of regular air circulation patterns which scientists call the El Niño–Southern Oscillation (ENSO). ENSO is believed to be one of the most important factors toward the western Pacific, causing the seas to stack up there. Sea levels around the Philippines rise until they are about 23 inches (60 cm) higher than sea levels off the coast of South America. Then the winds keep the westward-flowing water at the surface, where it gradually heats up. When this water finally reaches the western Pacific, it is the world's warmest ocean surface, usually above 82°F (28°C). In some areas, the temperature at the surface is as high as 89°F (31°C). As the Sun warms the ocean surface, moisture evaporates into the air in the gaseous form of water vapor. The warm water also heats air above the ocean, causing the air to rise. The extra warmth and moisture in the atmosphere increase the region's chance of heavy rainfall.

El Niño and weather patterns of the world

El Niño affects the ocean currents not just off the shores of South America, but right across the Pacific in the region of the equator (ih-KWAY-tuhr; an imaginary circle around Earth that divides it into two equal halves, called the northern hemisphere and southern hemisphere) and across the Indian Ocean to East Africa. The altered ocean currents affect weather conditions around the world.

El Niño brings torrential rains to some regions, including the central Pacific and Ecuador on the west coast of South America. To other areas, such as southern Africa, Australia, and northeast Brazil, it brings drought. In some places, the effects of El Niño are far-reaching, but not as predictable. For example, ENSO brings usually heavy rain to California in some years. In other years, it brings drought.

ENSO is more powerful and more destructive in some years than in others. The notorious El Niño of 1982 to 1983 brought great destruction around the world, with effects ranging from flooding to drought and famine. It caused surface sea temperatures near Peru to rise by 7°F (4°C). Australia experienced its worst drought of the century, and torrential storms struck the southwest United States. The 1982/1983 El Niño is thought to have killed

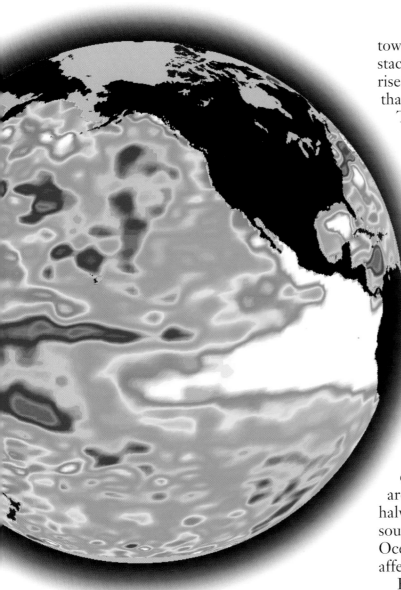

This false-color satellite image shows sea surface temperatures. The El Niño warm pool is in red.

in the variation of weather patterns around the world. ENSO can be worked out by measuring the difference between the air pressure at ground level at Darwin in northwestern Australia, and at Tahiti, midway across the Pacific. When air pressure is high at one of these places, it is low at the other. Every few years the pattern is reversed, as normal air circulation patterns break down. Thus, high-pressure air seesaws back and forth across the Pacific Ocean. This affects the trade winds that usually blow across the Pacific Ocean from east to west.

Trade winds affect temperatures and the water level in the oceans below. The winds push water

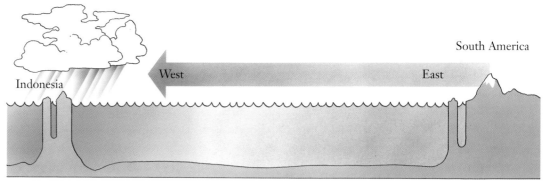

In normal years, the easterly surface winds on the equator keep the surface waters of much of the Pacific Ocean cool.

Indonesia — West — East — South America

During El Niño events, easterly winds weaken, so warmer water spreads eastward, bringing changes in rainfall distribution and other associated weather conditions.

Indonesia — South America

around 2,000 people and caused $13 billion in damage. More recently, 1997 to 1998 was another bad El Niño year, with a death toll of 2,100 and damage totaling $33 billion.

La Niña

La Niña is a Spanish phrase meaning "the girl." It is the name given to seasonal air and ocean currents in the Pacific that cause effects that are more or less opposite to El Niño. For example, in areas where El Niño brings flooding, La Niña causes drought. Regions that experience mild weather in El Niño years are buffeted by harsh weather in La Niña years. The effects of both are felt most strongly in winter.

During La Niña years, the trade winds blow westward from South America toward Asia more powerfully than usual. They push warm water along the equator to pool near Asia, causing heavy rain in the region. Strong La Niña winds also cause cold water to well up to the surface off the coast of South America. Cold water causes life in the sea to flourish but also decreases the rate at which moisture from the sea evaporates into the air above it. This brings drought to North and South America.

Records of air pressure readings at Darwin are also used to study La Niña. They suggest that El Niño and La Niña events alternate about every

two years, but the interval between powerfully affected years can vary from one to ten years.

Causes

Scientists are still trying to find out what causes El Niño and La Niña events. They have suggested that atmospheric changes in the South Pacific, variations in snowfall over Asia, and changing wave patterns in the Pacific are to blame. These theories confirm that weather patterns around the world are linked, but in ways not yet fully understood. Global warming, the gradual rise in Earth's temperature, may have caused an increase in atmospheric circulation. This, in turn, could be responsible for greater differences and extremes in wind patterns and in air and ocean currents.

Scientists hope to improve their ability to predict when El Niño and La Niña events will begin and how long they will last. A major research program investigating El Niño and La Niña was launched in 1992. Ships and aircraft from many countries cooperated in gathering information that should reveal more about these powerful ocean and air current systems.

CHECK THESE OUT!
✔AIR PRESSURE ✔OCEAN CURRENT
✔PACIFIC OCEAN ✔WEATHER ✔WIND

Glossary

absolute zero In theory, the lowest temperature that can be reached: −459.67°F (−273.15°C).

alkali (AL-kuh-ly) Salt that forms a solution in water with a pH level greater than 7. pH is a measure of acidity or alkalinity.

allergic reaction Unpleasant physical response to an otherwise harmless substance.

ammonite (A-muh-nyt) Extinct marine mollusk with a coiled shell. Many have been preserved as fossils.

archaeologist (AHR-kee-AH-luh-jist) Person who studies the material remains of past human life.

binary numbers System of numbers expressed in rows of zeros and ones.

brittle (BRIH-tuhl) Easily snapped or cracked.

colonize To take over an area and use its food sources.

conductor Material that allows electricity or heat to flow through it. *See also* insulator.

decimal numbers Number system that uses ten digits: zero through nine.

descendant (dih-SEN-duhnt) Individual who lives long after another member of the same family or species.

engineer (EN-juh-NEER) Person who designs mechanical, structural, or electrical devices.

flammable Easily ignited (set on fire) and burns quickly.

fusion (FYOO-zhuhn) When objects join to form a whole.

generator Machine that transforms mechanical energy into electricity.

infinite (IN-fuh-nuht) Having no end or limit.

insulator (IN-suh-LAY-tuhr) Material that is a poor conductor of electricity and heat. *See also* conductor.

irrigation Watering by artificial means, such as underground pipes, overhead sprinklers, or even by airplane.

landslide Rapid movement of rock or soil down a steep slope.

levee (LEH-vee) Bank of sediment deposited by a river along its bed and sides.

lunar (LOO-nuhr) Involving the Moon. Lunar vehicles, for example, are designed for use on the Moon. *See also* solar.

magnetic field Area around an object in which its magnetic forces can be detected.

mantle Layer of molten rock beneath Earth's crust.

metallic Containing a metal or having the properties of a metal.

meteor (MEE-tee-uhr) Effect seen from Earth when a meteoroid enters Earth's atmosphere and burns up.

meteorite (MEE-tee-uh-RYT) Rock particle from space that reaches Earth's surface.

meteoroid (MEE-tee-uh-ROYD) Rock particle in orbit around the Sun. It may enter Earth's atmosphere and burn up as a meteor. *See also* meteorite.

motor Machine that powers movement.

nutrient (NOO-tree-uhnt) Food necessary for an organism's life processes.

pitch Highness or lowness of sound.

shock wave Compressed wave (e.g., of sound) caused by a disturbance such as an explosion or an earthquake.

solar Involving the Sun. *See also* lunar.

sterilize (STEHR-uh-LYZ) To remove living microorganisms.

three dimensional Having height, length, and depth.

time zone Geographical region in which the same standard time is used.

Index

Page numbers in **boldface type** refer to main articles and their illustrations. Page numbers in *italic type* refer to additional illustrations.

550
EXP
#3

Exploring Earth and
Space Science

05/06	**DATE DUE**